The Bridge
spanning
Lake Maracaibo
in Venezuela

General Rafael Urdaneta Bridge

Bauverlag GmbH., Wiesbaden-Berlin

The prestressed and reinforced concrete bridge across Lake Maracaibo, Venezuela, is one of the largest in the world. It has a total length of 8,678m, five 235m main spans and 45m headroom. Never before has a bridge of such proportions been built as a reinforced and prestressed concrete structure.

Following two global tender actions, the Venezuelan Ministry of Public Works on August 15th, 1957 awarded to the Consorcio Puente Maracaibo (Maracaibo Bridge Joint Venture) the contract for the design and construction of the bridge. The Consorcio comprised Messrs Precomprimido C. A., Caracas, Venezuela, and Messrs Julius Berger A.G., Wiesbaden, Germany. Firms associated with the Consorcio included Messrs Grün & Bilfinger A.G., Mannheim, Philipp Holzmann A.G., Frankfurt a.M., and Wayss & Freytag K.G., Frankfurt a.M., all of Germany.

A design by Professor Ing. Riccardo Morandi, Rome, served as the basis for the structural analysis and detail plans. These were jointly prepared by the Consorcio and Professor Ing. Riccardo Morandi. Professor J. Kérisel, Paris, was engaged by the Consorcio to handle the particularly complex aspects of soil mechanics.

The National Laboratory of Portugal, Lisbon, was commissioned by the Venezuelan Government to carry out model tests to prove the fundamental principles and structural analysis results.

The examination of the structural analysis and working drawings prepared by the Consorcio and the control of design were entrusted by the Venezuelan Government to the late Professor P. Lardy, G. Schnitter, and Dr. F. Stüssi, of the Swiss Federal Polytechnic Zürich.

The excellent co-operation of all concerned made it possible to complete the prodigious construction, including all design work, within the contract time of forty months.

Fig. 1 *(Pages 2 and 3) View of Maracaibo. The bridge across the lake can be seen in the background*

Fig. 2 *Petroleum, Venezuela's liquid gold, is produced from land and offshore wells on pump*

Fig. 3 *It was pile dwellings of this type, on the shores of Lake Maracaibo, that persuaded the Spanish discoverers to call the country Veneciella, or Venezuela — little Venice*

Bridge Will Assist Communications and Economic Development

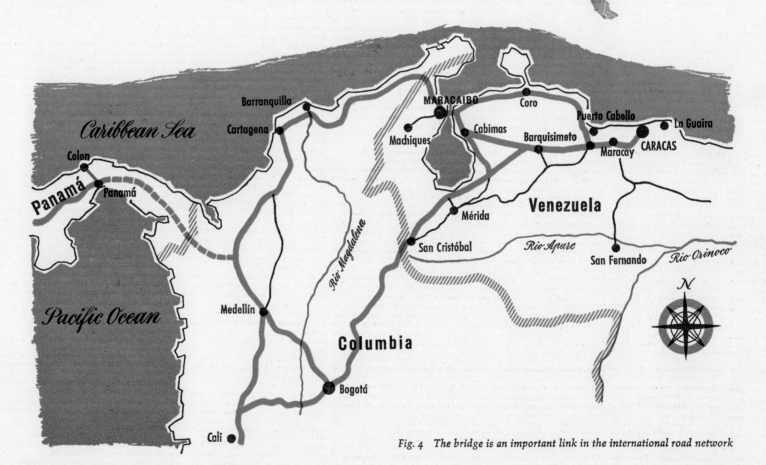

Venezuela has an annual petroleum production of 150 million tons, and in the Western World it is thus second only to the United States as a producer, and ranks first as a petroleum exporter. Seventy per cent of the oil produced comes from the Maracaibo area (fig. 2). There are other oil-bearing formations in the eastern part of the country where, near the river Orinoco, iron ore is additionally mined. The reserves are among the richest in the world, and the ores recovered are of exceptionally high grade.

Fig. 4   *The bridge is an important link in the international road network*

Therefore, like a number of other South American countries, Venezuela is an important producer of raw materials. And in order to provide adequate employment for its fast growing population, and to become independent of fluctuating international markets, Venezuela is making considerable efforts to expand its economy. However, the development of industry and agriculture, and the exploitation of mineral resources are hampered by the long distances to be travelled in difficult terrain. The country has a total area of 912,000 km², and 80 per cent of the seven million inhabitants live in the coastal region and mountainous hinterland comprising some 200,000 km². Consequently, economic development essentially calls for the construction of new, and the improvement of existing communications, to link up effectively the country's principal centres of production.

Fig. 5 The bridge links the oil country on the east shore of the lake with Maracaibo, capital of the state of Zulia

In addition, new and improved communications with neighboring countries are required to provide transportation facilities for the up and coming industries.

Improvement of the Pan-American Highway, comprising the Lake Maracaibo bridge, ranks high among the tasks to be tackled (fig. 4).

However, this bridge not only forms an important link of the International Carribean Highway; it is essential to the economic development of the state of Zulia, hitherto divided by Lake Maracaibo (fig. 5). Venezuela's major oil-fields are located in the eastern part of Zulia. There — between Cabimas and Mene Grande — petroleum from the inland and offshore wells is collected and piped, field-processed and transferred to oil tankers. The oil companies have their head offices, wharves, repair shops and utilities at Maracaibo, where, on the western shore of the lake, are also situated the harbour facilities and the international airport.

Maracaibo has grown at the same fast rate as the state in general. Its population of 120,000 in 1920 became 230,000 in 1950 and 460,000 in 1960.

In Venezuela more passenger and freight traffic is by road than by any other means. The population and industrial growth has produced an upswing in car and truck ownership. And in the past seven years the number of vehicles registered in Maracaibo has doubled (fig. 6).

Prior to the completion of the bridge, ferries plied between Maracaibo and the eastern shore of the lake. They had become incapable of coping with the swollen volume of traffic. As a result of this, the long-contemplated project for the construction of a lake-spanning bridge was realized.

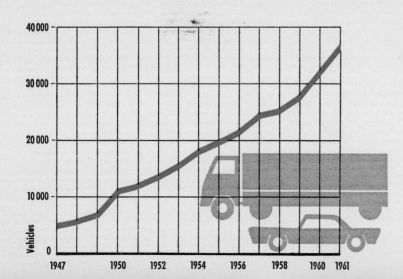

Fig. 6 Road vehicles are the most important means of transportation, and so the number of cars and trucks licensed in the Maracaibo area rapidly multiplied

From Planning to Contract Award

In the initial stage the Venezuelan Government carried out extensive investigations, to determine the most favorable point for crossing the lake, be it by bridge or tunnel. Routes A to E were tested with regard to topography of the lake bottom, type of subsoil, navigation requirements and, in particular, in respect of connection with Maracaibo's traffic system. The plan reproduced as fig. 7 gives the general layout of Maracaibo and the proposed development of the highway system, to take account of the city's rapid rate of growth.

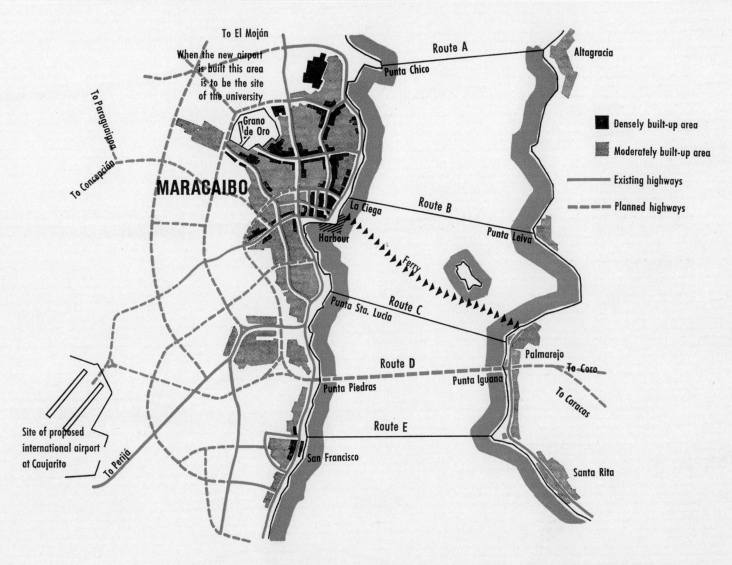

Fig. 7   Route D was decided upon because it provided the best solution of integration in Maracaibo's traffic system

Routes A and B constitute the shortest connections between the two shores; but as they are located between the sea and the port of Maracaibo, in an area much used by shipping, they were for this reason held to be unsuitable. Route C starts in a densely populated section of Maracaibo, where it would have been very difficult to link up with the highway system, and route E would have been too far from the city. Route D therefore provided the best solution in that it gives a direct connection between the new international airport and the oil-fields on the east shore of Lake Maracaibo. A further advantage of this route is that it runs at right angles to the shipway and direction of current, which makes navigation under the bridge much simpler.

Having thus established the most suitable location, the Government of Venezuela in 1956 called for bids for a 9,000 m long structure along route D. Bidders were invited to offer a bridge or a tunnel, or a combination thereof. The structure had to have four highway lanes, a single-track railroad and openings to provide adequate headway and waterway for shipping.

First International Tender Action in 1956

The ten firms invited to tender submitted eighteen widely varied designs.

Figures 8 to 11 show designs that would permit a continuous flow of road and rail traffic, regardless of shipping.

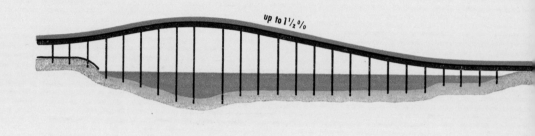

Fig. 8   Proposal 1. Most of the designs were for a bridge to handle both rail and road traffic, and on account of the former a gradient of 1¹/₂ per cent was chosen. In most cases a steelwork superstructure was proposed for the main spans

Fig. 9   Proposal 2. Other designs provided for a road and railway tunnel to pass under the main shipway, and for the tunnel to connect with a low bridge and an embankment on the east side

Fig. 10   Proposal 3. Another alternative was intended to obviate the technical difficulties of ventilating a road tunnel. Only rail traffic was to pass under the shipway; it was proposed to build a high-level bridge for road traffic. This bridge could have approach sections with gradients of up to 6 per cent, so that compared with proposal No. 1, the total length of the structure would be considerably reduced

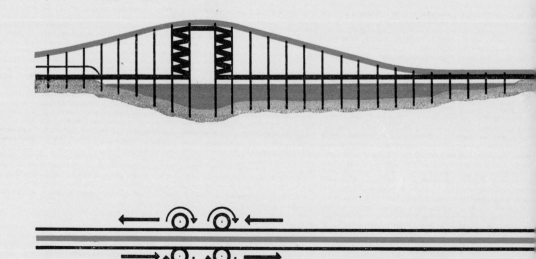

Fig. 11   Proposal 4. Yet another design provided for the rail traffic to be carried on a separate high-level bridge crossing the main shipway. Low-level sections on either side were to carry road traffic to the centre span. At each end of the centre span there would be steelwork towers incorporating spiral ramps to a separate high-level bridge. These spiral ramps would have a gradient of 4¹/₂ per cent

Designs based on discontinuous flow of traffic:

Other designs provided low level railway and road approach sections as far as the central spans. For rail traffic there was then a vertical lift bridge, and for road traffic a tunnel or a separate bridge to link the approach sections (figs. 12 to 15).

Fig. 12 Proposal 5. As shown in the illustration, this alternative was an arrangement by which a tunnel for road traffic would link the approaches

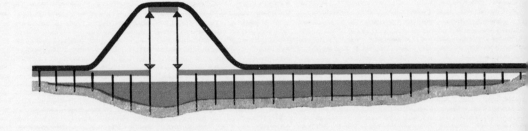

Fig. 13 Proposal 6. Another design provided for the road traffic to be carried on a separate high-level bridge having approaches with a 6 per cent gradient

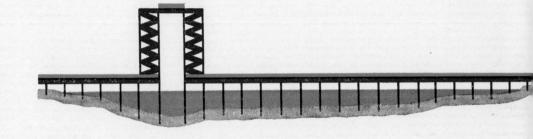

Fig. 14 Proposal 7. This version is a development of alternative No. 4. But whereas there would be the same facilities for road traffic, namely, spiral ramps to a high-level bridge. a vertical lift bridge would be provided for rail traffic

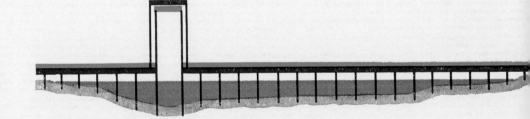

Fig. 15 Proposal 8. It was also proposed that there should be low-level spans on either side for road and rail traffic, and separate vertical-lift bridges across the main opening

Second International Tender Action in 1957

The tenders submitted during the first action had to be abandoned, because of fresh stipulations by the shipping and highway authorities. Accordingly, the Venezuelan Government in 1957 invited the same selected firms to submit new bids to take account of the changed conditions. It was specified that the free central span of the bridge should have a 400 m waterway, and that on either side of this there should be five openings each giving a waterway of 150 m. It was also specified that these eleven openings should have a 45 m vertical clearance and be located above the natural shipping channel.

Twelve bids were submitted; they ranged from 284 million to 760 million Bolivars. (At that time the exchange rate was 3.35 Bolivars to the American dollar).

With one exception, all the designs provided for a steelwork superstructure. Only the tender submitted jointly by Messrs Precomprimido C. A. and Julius Berger A.G. was based on an all reinforced and prestressed concrete structure (fig. 16); the designer was Professor Ing. Morandi.

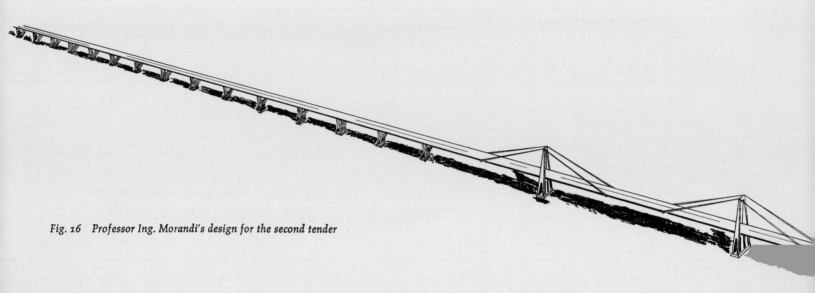

Fig. 16   *Professor Ing. Morandi's design for the second tender*

The reasons why the government commission recommended the acceptance of the bid by Precomprimido C. A. and Julius Berger A.G. were:

1. Greatly reduced maintenance costs. Because of the climatic conditions in the Maracaibo area, the annual upkeep of a steel superstructure was estimated at two million Bolivars.
2. The visual appeal of the design.
3. Less foreign exchange would have to be spent on imported materials.
4. A large number of Venezuelan engineers and skilled labour would be given the opportunity of acquiring experience in prestressed concrete practice.

Thus, on 25th May, 1957, the Venezuelan Government approved the design and accepted the bid of 329,580,136 Bolivars. And the finalized contract was signed in Caracas, on 15th August, 1957, by representatives of the Ministry of Public Works and of Messrs Precomprimido C.A. and Julius Berger A.G.

An immediate start was made on equipping the site, but in January 1958 operations had to be suspended because a new government came into power. The Ministry of Public Works utilized the intervening period to discuss with the contractors ways and means of reducing the construction costs. As there would have been no immediate need for a railroad track across Lake Maracaibo, it was decided that this part of the project should be dropped. This enabled considerable economies to be made. Also, at the request of shipping interests, the proportions of the main spans were amended. The design was revised to give five openings, each having a 200m width of waterway, and the original 400m wide central opening was deleted; the vertical clearance was to be 45m.

In April 1959 work was started on the agreed road bridge.

Climatic Conditions

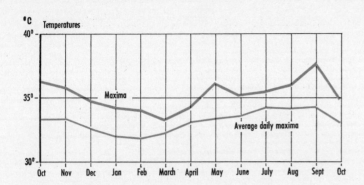

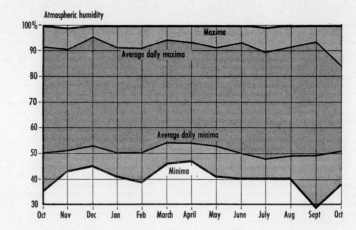

Fig. 17   Temperatures and atmospheric humidities at the site

Maracaibo is situated on a latitude of 10° 40' north, in a tropical climatic belt. There is thus little variation in temperatures (fig. 17). During the daytime the recorded temperatures range from 32° C to 37° C, and at night the thermometer drops by 5° to 7° C. As the average humidity is from 70 to 80 per cent, the climate is mostly very oppressive (fig. 17). There is an average annual rainfall of 560 mm, and this precipitation is accounted for by twenty to thirty cloudbursts.

The Gulf of Venezuela — the gateway to Maracaibo from the Caribbean Sea — is swept by the east trade winds peculiar to this latitude. At the construction site there is, however, a powerful current in the north-south direction, resulting from the variations in temperature and the consequent differences in atmospheric pressure over the Gulf of Venezuela and Lake Maracaibo (fig. 18). From December to April the winds, which have velocities of up to 13 m/s (47 km/h), blow mainly from the north to north-east (fig. 19). In the summer, as a result of tropical thunderstorms, wind velocities may exceed 30 m/s (108 km/h). In spite of periodic thunderstorms, the summer months are better for outdoor operations in the lake area, as then, if there is any wind at all it is seldom more than a gentle breeze (fig. 19). By contrast, the long windy periods in winter often necessitate the suspension of all difficult outdoor operations.

The tides in the Gulf of Venezuela effect variations of 10 to 20 cm in the water level at the construction site. And similar variations in the level of Lake Maracaibo occur between the rainy and dry seasons.

Fig. 18   Frequency of directions of wind during the year

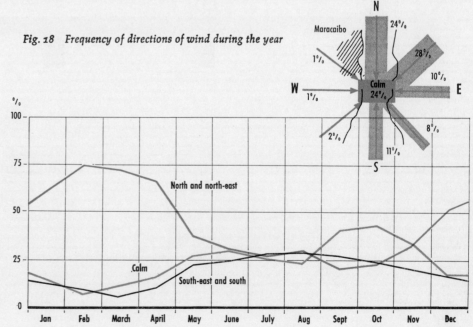

Fig. 19   Frequency of the main directions of wind in the individual months

Principles of the Winning Design

Superstructure

Maracaibo is not situated in a seismic area, but it is not immune to shock waves from earthquakes in adjacent regions.

Consequently, the employer required that, should one span of the bridge be affected by an earthquake disturbance, the adjoining spans would not also suffer damage.

Therefore, the design provided for all members to be of the statically determinate type, that is to say, girders on two supports and cantilevered girders.

In order to complete the 8,678 m long bridge in the short contract time, it was essential that, wherever possible, uniform members should be used. This enabled numerous units to be prefabricated at a plant on shore, specially equipped for the purpose. The same applied to large formwork and reinforcing units, thereby reducing costly in situ work to a minimum.

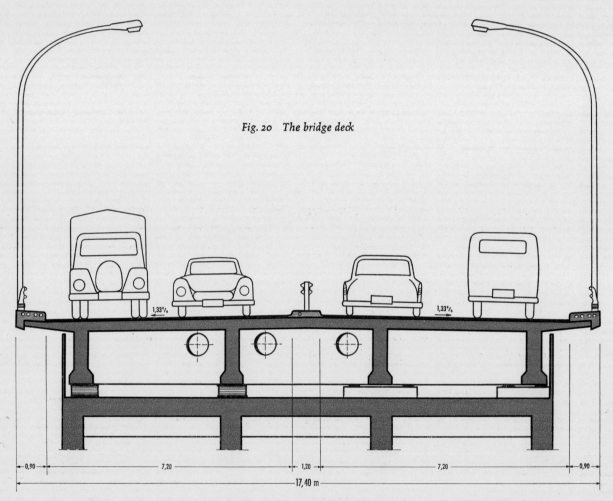

Fig. 20   The bridge deck

Starting from the low eastern shore, the structure features a 406 m long embankment, after which come twenty 36.60 m spans. This effective span was decided upon for the railway and road bridge, and had to be adhered to because the foundations had been completed when it was decided that the bridge should be for road traffic only (figs. 20 and 21).

Then follows a section having seventy-seven 46.60 m spans. Initially, this is 5.5 m above water level and then rises at a gradient of 0.4 per cent and ultimately at a gradient of 2.47 per cent to reach a height of 24 m (fig. 22). Up to this point the 46.60 m spans provide openings of balanced proportions. But if this span had been retained for the next section of the bridge, extending to a height of 50 m, the design would have been monotonous and the piers disproportionately high (See page 14).

Layout of bridge

Between Punta Piedras (western end) and
Punta Iguana (eastern end)

Effective span m	No. of openings	Length m
22.60	1	22.60
46.60	2	93.20
65.80	1	65.80
85.00	15	1,275.00
160.00	1	160.00
235.00	5	1,175.00
160.00	1	160.00
85.00	11	935.00
65.80	1	65.80
46.60	77	3,588.20
36.60	20	732.00
Embankment		406.00
	135	8,678.60

Fig. 22   The eastern section of the bridge is composed of 46.60m and 36.60m spans

Fig. 23 Piers of the 85m spans under construction. The cap of pier No. 12 is being concreted. Pier No. 11 is ready for mounting the cap shuttering

Therefore, the span was increased to 85m, and instead of plain piers, V and H trestle piers were employed; on top of them were mounted 39m long caps, thereby permitting the continued use of the 46.60m girders as suspended spans. As the height of the bridge increases, the V shape of the trestle piers is gradually transformed to an H by lengthening the pier legs in their lower parts (fig. 24). The size of the caps, V-sections of the piers and cross beams remains constant. Consequently, only minor changes were required in the centering, shuttering and reinforcement, from one pier to another. This facilitated and accelerated the construction operations.

Two special trussed steel centerings were fabricated for the caps. They had high-quality plywood shuttering. The shuttering and practically all the reinforcement were assembled on these centerings on land, and a complete service girder was placed in position with the aid of large floating cranes (fig. 23).

It was extremely difficult to bridge the navigation openings of 200m waterway and 45m headroom by a reinforced concrete structure. To this end, for the first time in the world, five large tied cantilever bridges of concrete, having 235m spans, were designed and constructed. The inclined ropes for the cantilevered girders pass over 92.5m high reinforced concrete towers (figs. 25 and 26).

Extensive investigations and calculations were necessary to determine the complex system of forces in the ropes, cantilevered portions and reinforced concrete towers.

Once again, the 46.60m girder was employed as suspended span between the 189.05m cantilever portions, so that this section of the bridge, too, is statically determinate.

Altogether, the 46.60m suspended girder was employed for one hundred and twelve large, medium and small-sized openings. In another twenty openings 36.60m girders were floated into position; they had been fabricated in the 46m mould that was shortened for the purpose.

Fig. 24 The trestle piers for the 85m spans gradually change from a V to an H shape with the increasing height of the bridge, but the caps and legs above the cross beams remain uniform in size

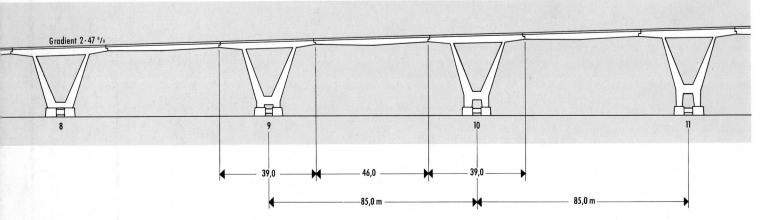

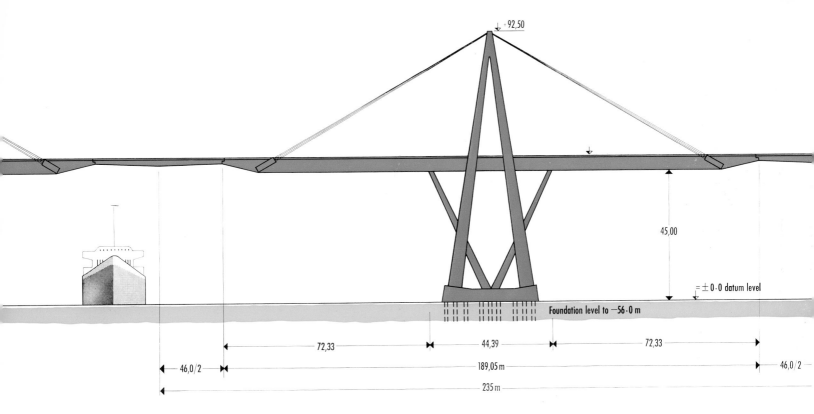

Fig. 25   There are 235m main spans. The deck is 50m above the lake level

Fig. 26   Piers of the main spans in the course of construction

Foundations

Over the main spans the depth of water reaches 17m in places; elsewhere it is mostly 10m to 12m, with a minimum of about 2m over the length of the embankment. The lake floor consists of sandy mud from 2m to 28m thick (fig. 21).

The deeper layer is formed by increasingly solid sand. Firm subsoil (terreno firme) — defined as subsoil capable of resisting twenty blows in the standard penetration test, and fifty blows 4m lower down — was encountered at depths varying from about 30m below sea level datum under the channel, to 45m below datum around the 6.7km mark. At both ends, the soil is firm at a depth of 10m or less. Numerous silt and clay lenses up to 10m thick are interspersed in the firm soil. There is frequent banding of sandstone and conglomerates in this sand. It is this banding of rock which was responsible for the steep shore of the western bridge-head locally known as "Punta Piedras", the "stony spit of land". About 90m below the water level there is a thick bed of hard clay, which runs upward between the sixth and seventh kilometre of the bridge.

It was particularly difficult to make the foundations for the 40,000-ton central piers, because of the thick clay and silt strata in the "firm soil" in this section of the bridge. Precast prestressed concrete piles, inserted in cased boreholes excavated by reverse circulation drilling rigs, were the only means of dependably transferring the immense loads through stratified sand, clay, silt and rock to the consolidated beds resistant to settlement. In order to keep the pile caps of the large piers as small as possible, the inserted piles had to have exceptionally high bearing power. By using a new injection method for placing the grout between the pile point and soil, ultimate load-bearing capacities of more than 2,000 tons were attained. A working load of up to 750 tons is imposed on these 135cm diameter piles in the finished structure.

Horizontal test loadings on the vertical piles revealed such a highly satisfactory degree of restraint in the upper layers of mud that batter piles could be dispensed with. Thus all the piles, even those up to 57.5 metres long, could be positioned in a single unit with the aid of large cranes. And instead of normal reinforced concrete piles cast in-situ, with

Fig. 27   The 250-ton crane of the "Elephant" floating work platform handling a 50m precast pile

Fig. 28 Workmen adjusting the control gear
of the 20-ton drop hammer

their inferior strength and quality difficult to control, pre-stressed units that had been precast at the land plant could be employed (fig. 27).

The development of this new-type inserted pile, and the supply and installation of the requisite heavy-duty plant entailed some delay before production could be started. Therefore, in the meantime, driven piles were used for the foundations at the shallow shores of the lake.

Reinforced concrete 50cm by 50cm driven piles were employed for the foundations of piers nos. 115 to 135, which are those for the 36m spans.

Hollow prestressed concrete piles, up to 35 metres long, having an outside diameter of 91.4cm and a wall thickness of 15.2cm were used for the deeper foundations required for piers nos. 1 to 19 for the 85m spans on the western shore. They were driven with 10- and 15-ton hammers. These piles had an imposed load of up to 300 tons.

The foundations for piers nos. 84 to 104 entailed exceptional difficulties in that the firm stratum in this section consists mainly of cohesive types of soil.

In clayey soil of this kind piles depend almost entirely on skin friction for carrying their load. Large-size inserted piles

thus have a small coefficient of efficiency. In addition, drilling operations in clammy and stiff clays are both tedious and time-consuming.

Driven steel piles were out of the question as steel corrodes at a rate of 1 to 2mm a year in the waters of Lake Maracaibo. According to the investigations carried out by the oil companies, the tropical temperatures cause ferrous metals to corrode even in the soil at the lake bottom. After detailed consideration and extensive testing, it was decided that the most dependable and economical foundation for this section would be hollow reinforced concrete driven piles of 91.4cm outside diameter, having a 12.7cm wall thickness.

A decisive aspect for the successful driving of these piles is the correct ratio of hammer to pile weight. Thus, for the first time in civil engineering history, use was made of a steam piling hammer having a drop weight of 20 tons. With the super-duty floating driver, piles up to 60m long were driven with such force that, in spite of the clayey subsoil, they were able to carry a working load of 220 tons (fig. 28).

Having successfully driven these piles, and in order to speed up the progress of work, driven piles were employed for the foundation of the 46.60m span piers.

General View of the site

1 Automatic concrete mixing plant — Johnson tower
2 Manufacture and storage of pile sections
3 Joining of pile sections and shipment of piles
4 Reinforcement bending yard
5 Gantry
6 Manufacture of bottom shuttering for pile caps
7 Placing reinforcement, pouring concrete, and stretching of 36.60m and 46.60m suspension girders

Fig. 29   The site

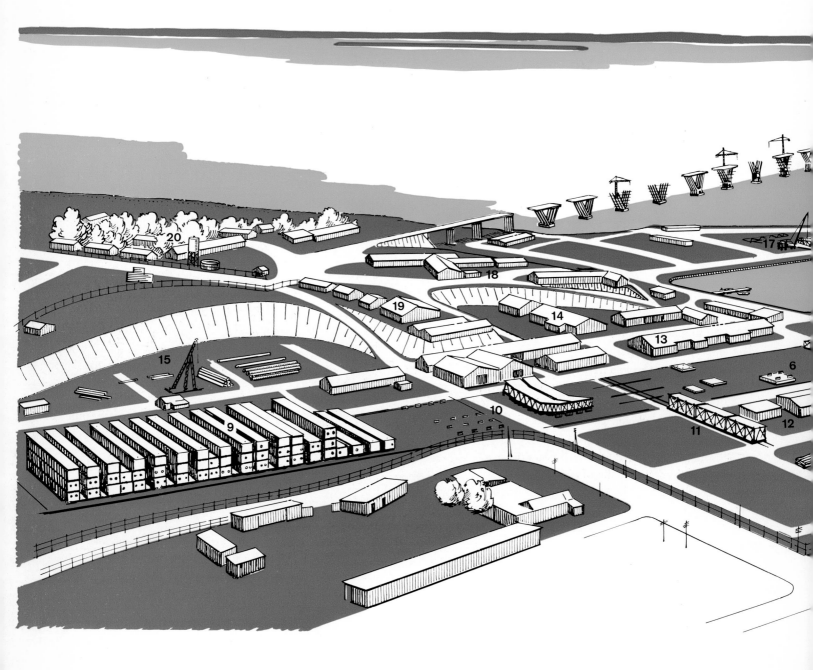

8 Shipping prefabricated members and service girders

9 Storing suspension girders

10 Manufacture of the shuttering for the pier cap girders of the 85m spans

11 Manufacture of the shuttering for the pier cap girders of the 235m spans

12 Joinery shop

13 Workshops

14 Stores

15 General storage yard

16 Control station for floating equipment

17 Assembly of centrings and shuttering for the cantilever arms of the 235m spans

18 Site offices

19 Concrete laboratory, soils laboratory, photo laboratory, first aid station, canteen

20 Camp

21 Bridge under construction

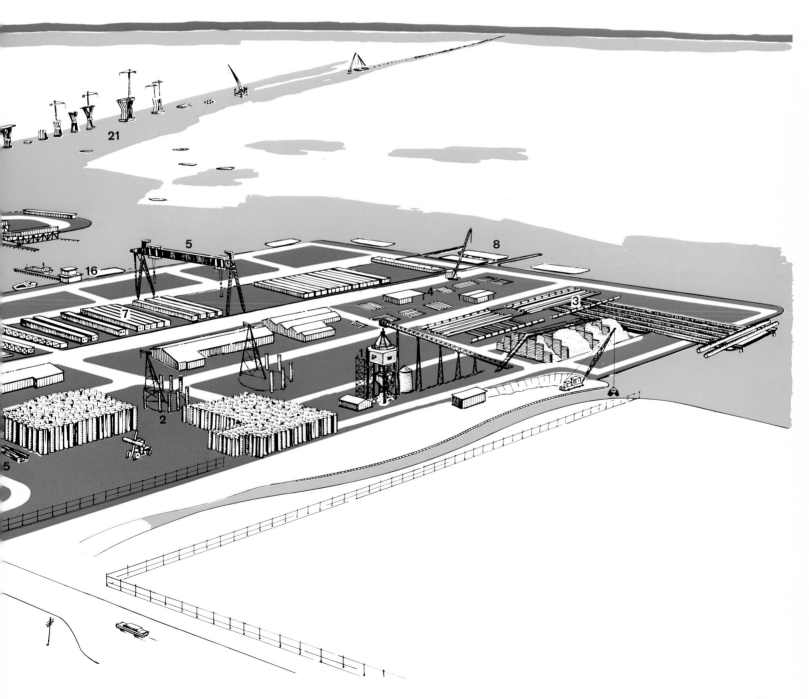

Fig. 30   Site seen from the air

Site Plant

It was originally planned to provide site facilities on either shore; but after detailed investigations this idea was abandoned. It was considered more expedient to erect the complete site plant on the west side, near Punta Piedras, 9 km away from the centre of Maracaibo.

To this end an area of 250,000 m² was prepared by hydraulic fill or, where there were rocky mounds, the ground was levelled by bulldozers. Six kilometres of bituminous roads were made to give access to the plant even in the rainy season (figs. 29 and 30). A carefully designed network of ditches and storm sewers ensured speedy, efficient drainage following heavy precipitation through cloudbursts, which occur regularly during the summer months.

Most of the site installation area was taken up by the plant for fabricating the precast concrete units. Its output in two years was in the region of 154,000 tons. It was serviced by an electric gantry having a 52 m span; this was capable of handling pieces weighing up to 200 tons over the length of its 600 m runway.

Quays 800 metres long were constructed to provide for the transshipment of plant, equipment, building materials and spares, the equipment of floating work platforms, together with facilities for floating cranes and other marine plant.

A radiotelephone system with numerous fixed and portable transceivers enabled the operations over the 9 km long site to be controlled and coordinated. Only by this means was it possible to program the movements of tugboats, lighters and floating cranes, and arrange for the efficient delivery of supplies at all the lake site locations.

To complete the unusually long bridge in the specified short contract time, it was necessary to purchase machinery, cranes, tugs, lighters, floating work platforms, together with numerous other items of equipment, to the value of more than 60 million bolivares. An extensive stock of spares had to be kept for the plant and equipment of American and European manufacture. The machine shops were equipped to handle the general run of repair jobs needed for the mechanical and electrical plant and equipment.

The nearest deposit of suitable gravel was located 62 km from the job site, in virgin forestland, but near a road. A plant was constructed for excavating, washing and screening the gravel (fig. 31). Other aggregates, obtained from the limestone quarries on the island of Toas, located 45 km to the north of the site, were transported by boat.

In the course of the construction operations, more than 100,000 tons of cement had to be transported from the cement works to the job site by means of trucks and special-type lighters.

The peak monthly power requirement on land was 264,000 kWh, which was obtained from the Maracaibo power station. The equipment on the piers and marine plant had an installed capacity of about 2,200 kVA.

The site engineering office was responsible for the many working drawings required for structural details and extensive auxiliary structures. Other office accommodation was provided for the senior executive and technical staff; a laboratory for concrete and soil tests was also erected.

Operations proceeded day and night, so that it was essential for engineers, foremen and skilled workers to be readily available if speedy decisions were required and immediate action was necessary. Therefore these men and their families were accommodated at a camp adjoining the construction site.

Fig. 31   Gravel plant

Design and Execution of the Foundations

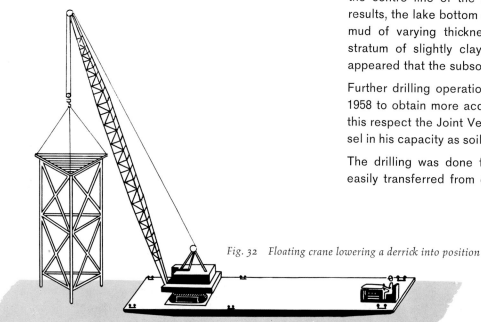

Fig. 32   Floating crane lowering a derrick into position

Soil Investigations

Included with the tender documents were the results of eleven tests carried out by the Standard Penetration method. The holes in question were drilled at intervals of about 900m on the centre line of the bridge route. According to the test results, the lake bottom consisted of a bed of unconsolidated mud of varying thickness, underneath which was the firm stratum of slightly clayey and silty sand. Consequently, it appeared that the subsoil was of uniform, satisfactory quality.

Further drilling operations were carried out in the spring of 1958 to obtain more accurate data on the foundation soil. In this respect the Joint Venture was advised by Professor Kéri-sel in his capacity as soil mechanics consultant.

The drilling was done from rigs that could be quickly and easily transferred from one location to another with the aid

Fig. 33   Rig for drilling into the subsoil

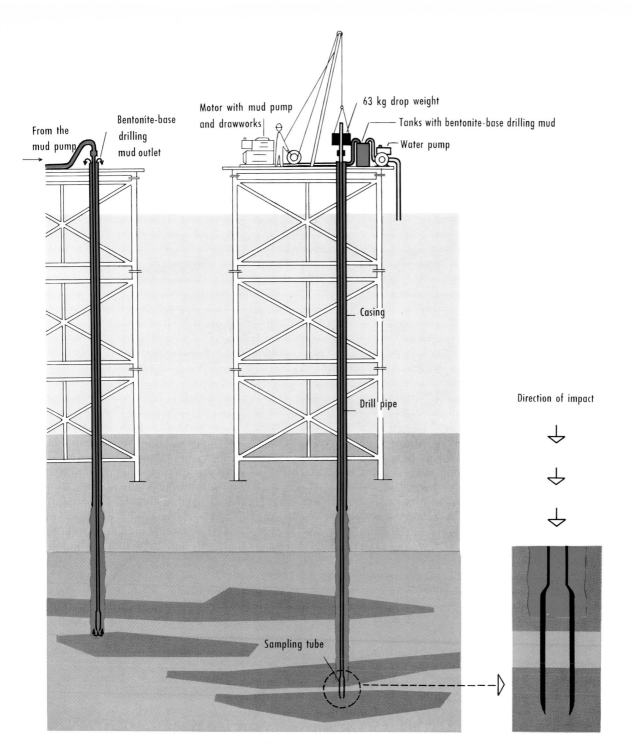

Motor with mud pump and drawworks

63 kg drop weight

Tanks with bentonite-base drilling mud

Water pump

From the mud pump

Bentonite-base drilling mud outlet

Casing

Drill pipe

Direction of impact

Sampling tube

Fig. 34 Hole drilled with mud circulation and soil sample taken by standard penetration test

of floating cranes (fig. 32). The triangular derricks were steel tubular welded fabrications having sides 6 m long. Additional 3 m or 6 m sections were bolted to the parent unit to suit the depth of water at the drilling location. When necessary, the derricks were anchored in position by guy ropes fastened to concrete blocks in the lake bed.

The drilling methods used were those customary in the United States since both the equipment and experienced drilling crews were locally available (fig. 33).

The section of the bore holes penetrating the mud was cased off, and drilling of the bearing stratum was then continued by the circulating fluid method. By employing a bentonite suspension as the drilling mud, the hole side was prevented from caving in (fig. 34). The following were carried out in the bore hole:

a) Standard Penetration Test (SPT)

b) Removal of undisturbed soil samples by means of thin-walled Shelby samplers, should this be necessary

c) Cone penetrometer tests

Standard Penetration Test

A 2in. bit was normally employed for drilling the holes. For the purpose of the standard penetration test an SPT sampler was fixed to the base thread of the drill pipe (fig. 34). By dropping a 63 kg weight from a height of 75cm onto an anvil on the drill pipe, the number of blows required to drive the sampling tube 30cm into the soil was determined. The drill pipe was then run out of the hole and the sample removed from the tube (fig. 35). The SPT method proved very satisfactory for obtaining soil data at this job site.

On the basis of the SPT soil samples the particle-size distribution curves, Atterberg limits, and moisture contents were

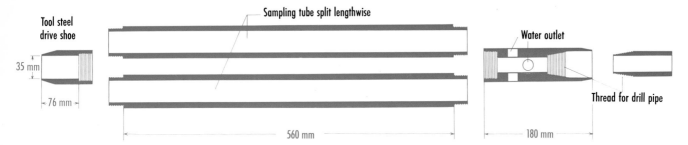

Tool steel
drive shoe

Sampling tube split lengthwise

Water outlet

Thread for drill pipe

35 mm

76 mm

560 mm

180 mm

Fig. 35   Sampling spoon for standard penetration test

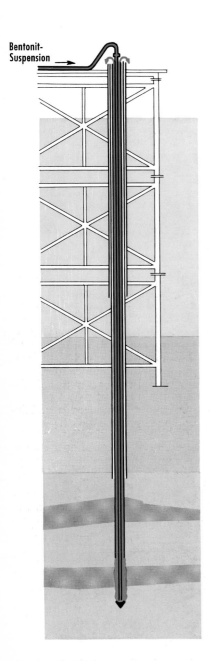

Bentonit-
Suspension

*Fig. 36   Conical penetrometer
with betonite-based mud circulation*

determined. The number of blows indicated the density of the sand strata and plasticity of the clay; adequate laboratory analyses of undisturbed soil samples were performed for checking purposes. As a rule, an SPT was carried out at intervals of 1.5m of hole drilled.

Taking Undisturbed Soil Samples

Undisturbed soil samples were taken with Shelby tube samplers of a type similar to German samplers. The sampling tubes were 58.5cm long and had a wall thickness of only 1.6mm. This ensured maximum protection to the samples, in spite of the hole size of only 2 in.

The 14 per cent Hvorslev area ratio C_a of these samplers was adequate. A better area ratio C_a was obtained when drilling supplementary comparative holes of 4in. and 6in. diameter. The 6 per cent area ratio C_a of the 4in. Shelby sampler was very good.

Cone-penetration Tests

Resistance to the penetration of a cone was measured with a 4.6cm diameter conical penetrometer (fig. 36). A resistance of 100 kg/cm² corresponded to about 50 blows of the SPT. In the sandy subsoil the sensitive penetration tests indicated sandstone-like cementations and stratifications of thin, soft clay.

Rotating-auger Shear Tests

The vertical piles exhibited partial restraint in the soft mud at the lake bottom. The cohesion of this mud was determined with a rotating-auger tester of our own production (fig. 37). According to the tests performed, the cohesion was 0.05 kg/cm² at the lake bottom and increased to 0.4 kg/cm² with the depth.

24

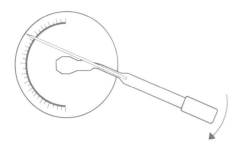

Holes Drilled				
Hole diameter in.	No. drilled	Total length m	Average length of drill pipe m	Linear metres drilled
2	202	11,939	59.11	9,767
4	42	3,257	77.55	2,633
6	2	100	50.25	100

Standard penetration tests were carried out in all holes. Additionally, undisturbed soil samples were taken as follows, by means of Shelby samplers: —

219 of 2in. dia.; 127 of 4in. dia. and 8 of 6in. dia. Forty-six holes were deeper than 80m, and six more than 90m deep. The maximum depth drilled was 90.85m. Cone resistance was tested in more than 30 bore holes.

The cross-section shown as fig. 21 on page 12 a was produced on the basis of the drilling and test program. For the sake of clarity, only a few of the SPT values and cone resistance measurements are indicated.

Analysis of the Soil Samples

The soil samples were analysed at the site laboratory. As small-size holes were drilled, conforming to American practice, the laboratory was supplied with American test equipment (fig. 38).

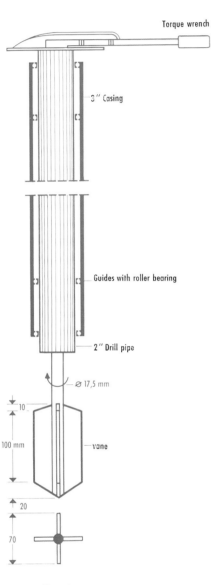

Fig. 37 Rotating auger tester

Fig. 38 Angle of internal friction and cohesion of an undisturbed soil sample are determined by triaxial shear test

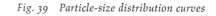
Fig. 39   Particle-size distribution curves

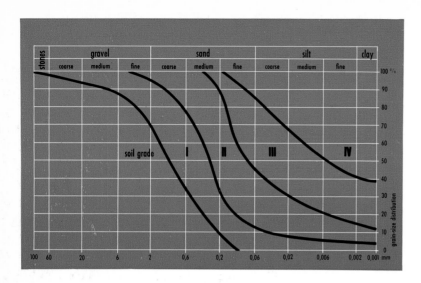

The soils were divided into four classes according to their particle-size distribution (fig. 39). All the samples taken along the bridge route had a fairly high percentage of ultra-fine particles, which explains the flat particle-size distribution curves. The classification was as follows: —

Grade   I   Silty medium to coarse sand
Grade   II   Silty fine sand with clay
Grade   III   Clayey silt with fine sand
Grade   IV   Silty clay

This system of classification proved to be satisfactory. In nearly all cases the grading curves of the samples were entirely within the specified range. Consequently, most of the soils could be classified according to their 50 per cent fraction. Comparisons between samples taken with the SPT and Shelby samplers revealed no systematic deviations in the grading curves.

In addition to the grading curves, the Atterberg limits and the moisture content of the SPT samples were determined in the laboratory.

The following results were obtained: —

Soil grade   I   Atterberg limit not definable
Soil grade   II   Mostly impossible to define the Atterberg limit
Soil grade III   PI between 17 and 22
                      LI between 26 and 50
Soil grade IV   PI between 15 and 23
                      LI between 30 and 62

In so far as it was necessary, the undisturbed samples were tested for

Specific gravity
Atterberg limits
Moisture content
Dry density
Voids ratio
Percentage of water saturation
Unconfined compressive strength
Angle of internal friction and cohesion
Modulus of volume change

The test results were as follows

Soil grade	I	II	III	IV
φ Degrees	33 to 37	27 to 33	22 to 27	14 to 22
Cohesion in kg/sq.cm.	0.0 to 0.1	0.1 to 0.3	0.3 to 0.6	0.6 to 1.4

Permeability of soil grade IV $k = 0.6 \times 10^8$ cm/s

Mean moduli of volume change

Load in kg/cm²	1—2	2—4	4—8	8—16
		Moduli of volume change in kg/cm².		
Soil grade I	198	299	428	671
II	102	230	273	448
III	116	158	209	345
IV	158	142	184	253

The high moduli of volume change of the grades III and IV under a small imposed load can be explained by the chemical consolidation and high geological preloading.

Testing Driven Piles, Cast-in-the-ground Piles and Piles Placed in Pre-drilled Holes

Fig. 40   A cast-in-the-ground pile
of 1m dia. is loaded with 1,100 tons

The conventional driven or cast-in-the-ground piles were un-suitable for transmitting the heavy foundation loads to deeper soil layers. This meant that new-type piles had to be developed, which called for extensive testing. To start with, three B 1m cast-in-the-ground piles were put down on land. They were loaded by a large tank filled with sand that was kept in the horizontal by four hydraulic jacks (fig. 40). The piles were embedded from 5.5m to 16.5m in the firm stratum, and the maximum imposed loads ranged from 800 to 1,100 tons which, however, resulted in more than 10cm settlements. It was thus obvious that non-driven piles could be used for transmitting heavy loads, under the soil conditions obtaining, if the considerable amount of settlement could be reduced.

Four driven piles and five piles placed in pre-drilled holes were used for testing at pier 12, about 100m north of the centre line of the bridge.

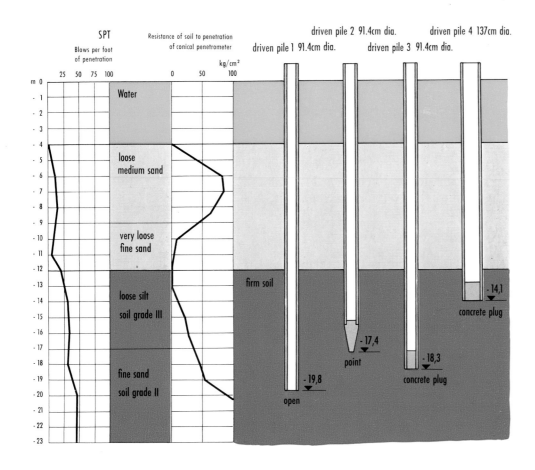

Fig. 41   Driven test piles at station 0.830km
(about 100m north of the centre line of the
bridge)

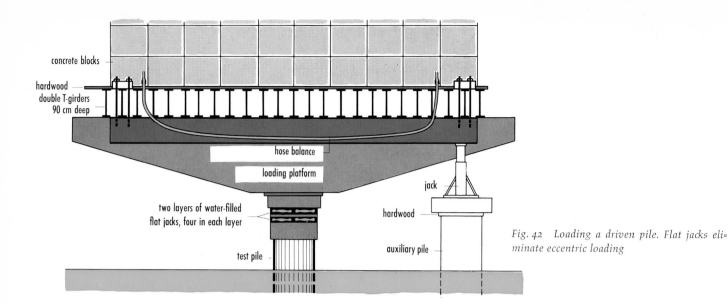

concrete blocks

hardwood
double T-girders
90 cm deep

hose balance

loading platform

jack

two layers of water-filled
flat jacks, four in each layer

hardwood

test pile

auxiliary pile

*Fig. 42   Loading a driven pile. Flat jacks eli=
minate eccentric loading*

Test Loading of Driven Piles

Three driven piles had a diameter of 91.4cm, the fourth 135cm (fig. 41). They were prestressed in longitudinal direction, their wall thickness being 12.7cm and the crushing strength of the pile concrete 600 kg/cm² as determined on test cubes. Piles 1 and 2 were driven with a 15-ton hammer at a drop of 45cm to a penetration of 17mm under the last ten blows. Pile 1 had an open end at the bottom, pile 2 had a concrete shoe. Under equally hard driving, pile 1 penetrated 2m deeper into the ground than pile 2, but the soil forced into the hollow pile shaft caused a longitudinal crack.

Piles 3 and 4 were closed at the bottom by a flat concrete plug. They were driven with an 8-ton hammer only, but at a drop of 1m to a penetration of 7mm under the last ten

blows. But in spite of even the hardest driving, pile 4 could not be driven to the firm fine sand because the ratio of hammer weight to pile weight of 0.27 was too unfavourable, especially in view of the large base area of this pile 4. The test load was transmitted to the pile by means of a loading platform carrying twenty-five to thirty double T-girders, 90cm deep, on which concrete blocks were stacked (figs. 42 and 43). When settlements occured, hydraulic jacks were continuously adjusted to make sure that a slight pressure was always exerted by the test load on the jacks whose levels were always checked by hose balances.

To avoid an inclined loading platform inducing an eccentric force into the pile, two layers of water-filled flat jacks were

Fig. 43   Loading a base

provided between load and pile. These flat jacks were connected to each other by copper pipes.

Pressure gauges connected to each flat jack layer permitted checking the loads on the pile (fig. 42).

Loading pile 1 had to be discontinued at 450 tons and pile 2 at 550 tons because of shortage of concrete blocks (fig. 44). The open-ended pile 1 showed the least settlement, but owing to the danger of longitudinal cracks, open-ended piles had to be discarded.

Settlements of piles 2 and 3 were in good accordance. Since the ultimate load of these piles was more than 600 tons, their working load in sandy soils was fixed at 270 to 300 tons. The large settlement of pile 4 proved that driven piles of this size did not yield satisfactory results technically and were therefore uneconomical (fig. 44).

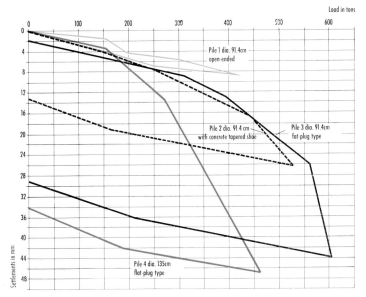

Fig. 44   Settlements of driven test piles at station 0.830km

Test Loading of Piles Placed in Pre-drilled Holes

For these piles, steel casings of 1.50m dia. were sunk to the desired depth and the soil within removed by grab or reverse circulation drilling. The piles were then placed and the space between pile and firm soil was grouted while the casing was withdrawn (fig. 45). Pile 1 had a loose shoe which, after the hardening of the skin grout, compacted the underlying soil by driving it to refusal thus reducing settlements. This driving, however, proved very difficult and damaged the pile bottom. To measure point resistance, flat jacks were installed in the bottom of pile 2 (fig. 46).

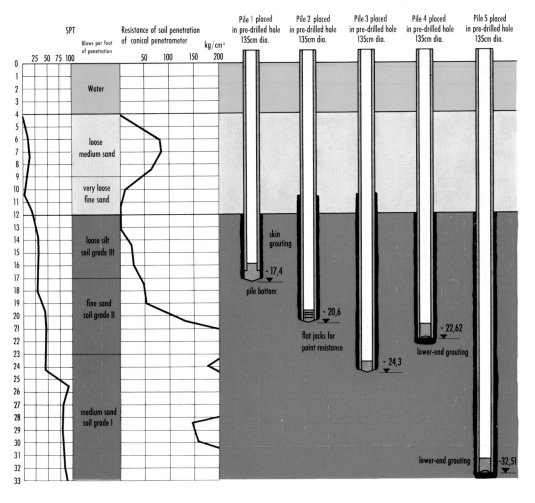

Fig. 45   Test piles placed in pre-drilled holes at station 0.830km

29

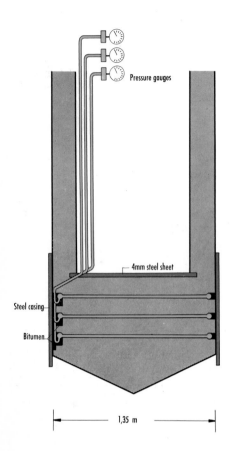

Fig. 46 Point resistance at all load increments was measured by flat jacks arranged in three layers in bottom of pile 2

Pressure gauges

4mm steel sheet

Steel casing

Bitumen

1,35 m

Measurements of friction between ground (sandstone and iron oxyde layers) and grouted skin surface showed values of 8 to 14 tons/m².

The pile settled 18.2cm at a load of 1,357 tons (fig. 47).

At a settlement of 10mm, the pile carried 490 tons, 357 tons of which, or 76.5 per cent, were absorbed by skin friction and 23.5 per cent only by point resistance (fig. 48). Point resistance amounted to only 6.7 kg/cm² at 10mm settlement and increased at 18.2cm settlement to 44.4kg/cm². Thus the pile, like most non-driven piles, carried its load under the admissible settlements almost by skin friction alone. In order to raise the load-carrying capacities of the piles, a means had to be found to mobilise the point resistance long before settlements between 10cm to 20cm are obtained.

To achieve this, a method of pressure grouting of the lower end of the pile was developed (figs. 49 and 50). This lower end was filled with concrete to a height of 1.50m and a star-shaped grouting chamber was provided there. Two 1 in. grouting pipes were connected to the top of the chamber, whose bottom was closed by a steel plate.

After the pile was firmly bonded to the firm soil through skin grouting, it was then grouted beneath the lower end. Grout was injected into the inlet pipe until all water was forced out of the grouting pipes. Then the outlet pipe was closed and the grouting pressure raised to 40 kg/cm².

Generally, the grouting force between lower pile end and soil underneath was increased to the future working load, while the pile was continuously checked with a level. If the grouting

Fig. 47 Settlements of pile 2 placed in pre-drilled hole

Fig. 48 Point resistance and skin friction of pile 2 under load

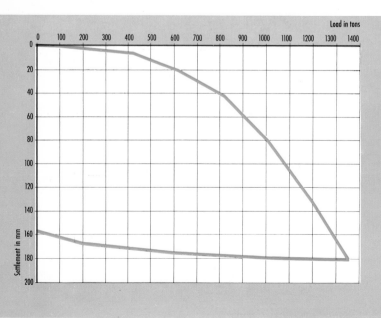

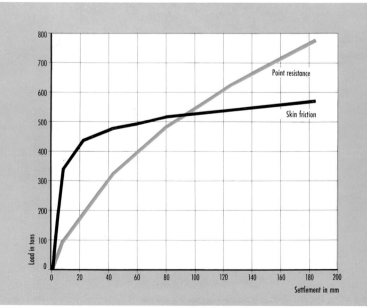

Point resistance

Skin friction

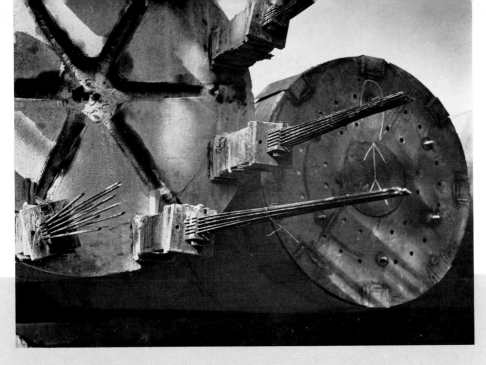

Fig. 49 The left pile is being assembled and its grouting chamber is still open, whereas this chamber is already closed by a base plate on the right pile

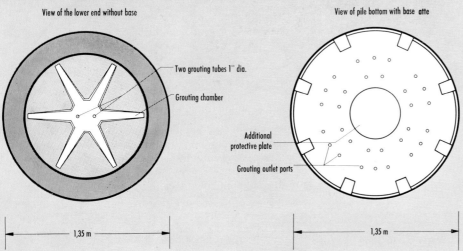

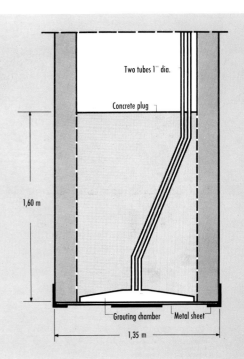

Two tubes 1" dia.

Concrete plug

1,60 m

Grouting chamber   Metal sheet

1,35 m

View of the lower end without base

Two grouting tubes 1" dia.

Grouting chamber

1,35 m

View of pile bottom with base atte

Additional protective plate

Grouting outlet ports

1,35 m

Fig. 50   Bottom-grouting arrangement

Fig. 51   Settlements of piles placed in pre-drilled holes with and without lower-end grouting

force lifted the pile not more than 10mm, the skin friction was at least as large as the working load and the coefficient of safety was at least 2.

Piles 4 and 5 were the first to be pressure-grouted by this new method, for which a patent has been applied for. Pile 4, which is embedded 10cm in firm soil, carried an ultimate load of 1,620 tons (fig. 51). Pile 5 was loaded with 2,006 tons — to our knowledge the largest test load in the world — without having got anywhere near the ultimate load. Still more important than the high ultimate loads of these piles with pressure-grouted lower ends were the considerably lower settlements within working loads from 500 to 1,000 tons.

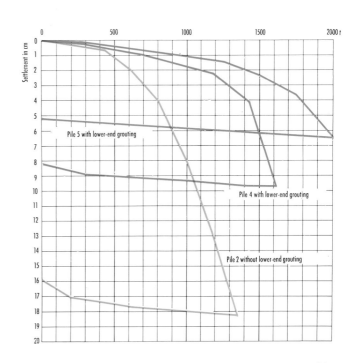

Pile 5 with lower-end grouting

Pile 4 with lower-end grouting

Pile 2 without lower-end grouting

Settlement in cm

Fig. 52 A lower-end grouted pile placed in a pre-drilled hole was tested with 2,006 tons, but even this record load has not got anywhere near the ultimate load

Test loads on piles placed in pre-drilled holes were considerably higher than those on driven piles. Therefore, the loading platform on such a pile had to be kept horizontal by four hydraulic jacks (figs. 52 and 53).

Since at all load increments the settlements were allowed to die out, a test loading lasted up to 23 days. During this period, checking was done day and night and the testing rig kept horizontal by the jacks.

Settlements of the piles placed in pre-drilled holes were — as for the driven piles — measured by means of levels in respect to bench marks set some distance away from the test piles. Ten measurements were taken each time and their mean value computed so that the mean error of one series of ten measurements amounted to only 0.3mm. Settlements could not be measured by the bootstrap test because the steel girder (yoke) would have shown deflections of several millimetres due to temperature differences.

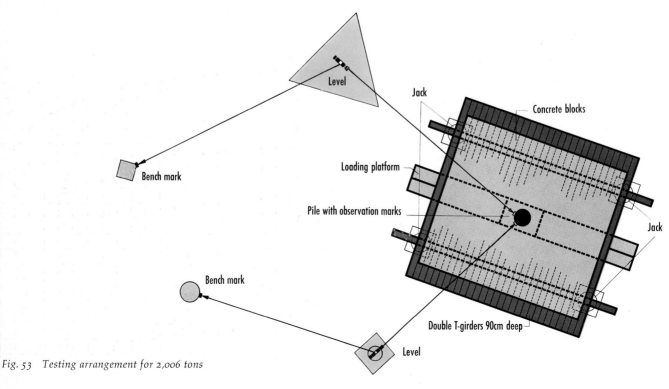

Fig. 53 Testing arrangement for 2,006 tons

Computation of Ultimate Loads

The ultimate bearing capacity of a pile can be expressed by the equation $P_s = F_s \cdot Nq \cdot \Sigma\gamma \cdot h$, where

P_s = ultimate bearing capacity of pile point
F_s = pile point area
Nq = coefficient
$\Sigma\gamma \cdot h$ = geological compression of the soil at the depth of the pile point

It was assumed hitherto that Nq depended primarily on the angle of internal friction of the soil.

The load tests conducted in Maracaibo, which embraced small cone penetrometers and various piles up to very large diameters, revealed that Nq is greatly influenced by the pile diameter (fig. 54).

The lengths of the piles placed in pre-drilled holes were therefore computed as follows (fig. 55):

1. Pile loads

a) Loads from the superstructure.
In most cases, the heaviest loads resulted from a combination of bridge dead load, asymmetric traffic load, and wind pressure transversely to the centre line of the bridge.

b) Pile weights.
In most cases, the dead weight of the piles filled with concrete exceeded 100 tons and could therefore not be neglected.

c) Negative skin friction.
Consolidation of the mud produced a negative skin friction of 1 ton/m² resulting in pile loads of 80 tons to 140 tons. This was found after extensive investigations.

2. Skin friction and point resistance

a) Skin friction.
According to the measuring results, 8 tons/m² were considered to be a safe value.

b) Point resistance.
The maximum resistance $ps = Nq \cdot \Sigma\gamma \cdot h$ was taken from the diagram of Professor Kérisel (fig. 54).

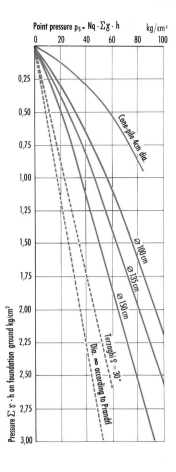

Fig. 54 Limit value of point pressure in dependence of embedment in firm soil of at least 8m and diameter of piles according to Professor Kérisel. The curves refer to compact fine sand having an angle of internal friction of 30°

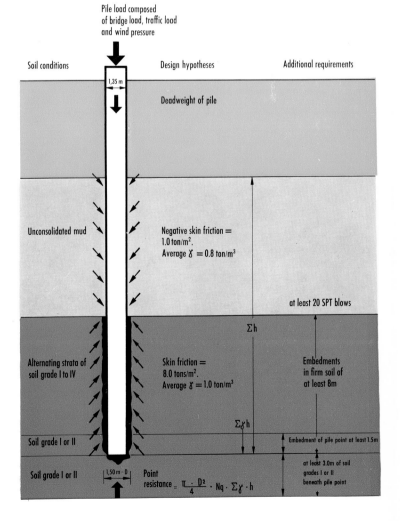

Fig. 55 Load and skin friction and point resistance for single pile

3. Safe design

a) Safe design for single pile.

The bearing capacity thus calculated refers to a single pile only. According to Whitaker, different coefficients of reduction have to be used for the pile groups. The coefficient of reduction happened to be 0.8 for all pile groups of the Maracaibo bridge. If the safety design of a single pile was 2.70, the safe design of a group was 2.16.

b) Safe design for pile groups.

The arithmetic safety design for pile groups was supposed to be 2.0. Actually, the safeties are higher, since a minimum value was used for skin friction only.

4. Additional conditions for determining pile lengths

Pressure grouting around pile points required sandy soil so as to allow ready evacuation of pore water during grouting and to produce thus prestressing of the soil and not only of the pore water. The method of calculation developed by Professor Kérisel also assumed sandy soil around pile point.

Therefore, sand layers from 1.50m above to 3.0m below the pile point were a prerequisite.

Point grouting was improved to such an extent that piles only settled 7mm to 11m under 860 tons test load. 7mm had to be attributed to elastic shortening of the pile, so that the permanent settlement of the pile after removal of the load amounted to 0.5 to 2.0mm only.

Horizontal Test Loading

The prestressed piles placed in pre-drilled holes of 135cm dia. can be considered to be halfway between piles and caissons and can absorb bending moments up to 150 mt. To take full advantage of this, the bridge was founded on vertical piles. Thus the number of piles was reduced and operations of drilling and placing made easier. Test loads, however, had to prove whether the vertical piles would transmit the horizontal bridge loads to deeper soil layers by restraint.

Fig. 56 Two piles placed in pre-drilled holes are subjected to a reciprocal traction force of 7.5 tons

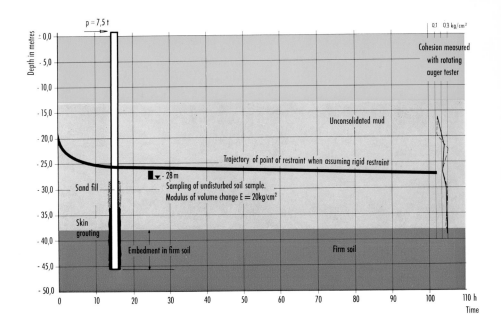

Fig. 57 Result of horizontal test loading

Two 46m piles placed in pre-drilled holes and embedded only 8m in firm soil were subjected to a reciprocal traction force of 7.5 tons (fig. 56). This produced a bending moment in the pile fifty per cent higher than that caused by the horizontal forces of the superstructure. Measurements of movements and deflections of the piles proved that the greatest part of their horizontal loads was transmitted to the mud, a result which agreed favorably with similar tests made in the Lake of Maracaibo by the oil companies. Since the restraint of a pile in the soil moves downward in the course of time, the maximum horizontal loads were allowed to exist more than 100 hours; i. e. considerably longer than the short-period horizontal loads of the bridge resulting from traffic and wind (fig. 57).

Further Load Tests

During the construction of the foundations, the employer demanded numerous additional load tests in which the piles were loaded with the dead load and two times the forces resulting from wind and traffic. Higher loads would at a later stage have caused additional stresses in the completed structure on account of smaller settlements of these preloaded piles.

A driven pile of pier 92 was subjected to the longest load test. It was to be determined whether driven piles of 91.4cm dia. would be suitable for foundations in the clay encountered here. The pile was loaded for 36 days, 12 of them with 450 tons.

The following tests were carried out:

	No.	Load in Tons
1. Basic load tests		
cast-in-the-ground test piles put down on land	3	up to 1,100
test piles placed in pre-drilled holes		
at station 0.830km	5	up to 2,006
driven test piles at station 0.830km	4	up to 600
2. Load test on pier piles		
driven piles 50cm square	5	up to 180
driven piles 91.4cm dia.	12	up to 450
driven pile group (pile dia. 91.4cm)	2	up to 266 per pile
piles placed in pre-drilled holes 135cm dia.	16	up to 860
horizontal loads on piles placed in pre-drilled holes	2	up to 7.5
A total of 49 pile tests were made		

Embankment at Punta Iguana

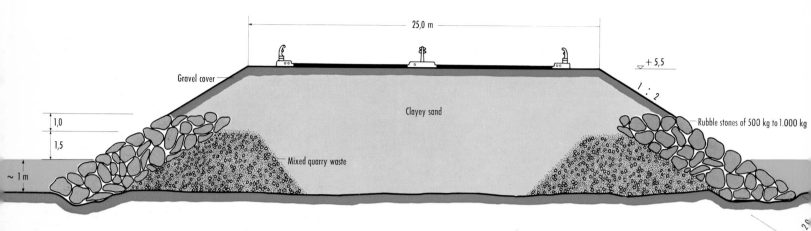

Fig. 58   Cross-section through embankment at Punta Iguana

Water depth near the eastern shore at Punta Iguana did not allow the use of a floating pile driver. Therefore, an embankment of 406m length was built. Prof. Brezina of the University of Caracas determined by hydraulic model tests the best way of protecting the slopes of the embankment against wave action. Tests with various types of rubble with or without asphalt sealing and with roughened concrete slabs proved that rubble stones for slope protection should weigh not less than 250 kg.

Up to 2.50m above mean lake level, the slopes were protected by rubble stones of 500 to 1,000 kg (fig. 58). A filter bed of mixed quarry waste prevents erosion of the sand core. The core of the embankment consists of clayey sand which in the modified Proctor test obtained a dry density of 2.1 to 2.25. The soil was compacted by sheepsfoot rollers to 95 per cent of optimum Proctor density. Its moisture content was always kept at an optimum in spite of the greatly varying evaporation. Dry density and compactness were continuously checked (fig. 59).

Fig. 59   Testing compactness during fill operations

Driven Pile Foundations

To speed up construction work, the bridge was partially founded on driven piles. Whereas for the low 36m spans near the eastern shore ordinary reinforced concrete piles 50 × 50cm were sufficient, the piers of the 46m and 85m spans required hollow prestressed concrete piles of 91.4cm outside dia. and 12.6cm or 15.2cm wall thickness. Pile driving was done by Messrs Heerema C.A. and Messrs Raymond Brown & Root as subcontractors.

Fig. 60 Raymond Brown & Root on-site pile casting yard. Placing a spinning form

Fig. 61 Section through driven pile

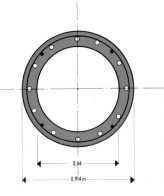

Concrete plug

Ondulated surface

1,20   0,30

4,88 m

0,66

0,914 m

Fig. 62 Pile reinforcement and inside form panels are in place on left prestressing bed. Reinforcement is placed in centre of picture and piles of the third prestressing bed have just been stripped. Piles are stockpiled by gantries at one end of the prestress yard. Anchorage for tensioning wire is seen in foreground.

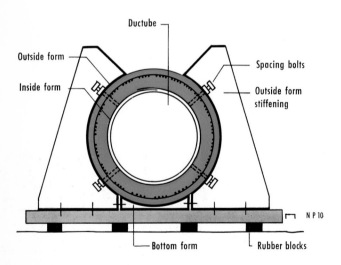

Fig. 63   Cross-section of pile on prestressing bed

Fig. 64   Pile casting on prestressing bed. Concrete is compacted by internal and external vibrators

Fabrication of Driven Piles

Messrs Raymond Brown & Root spun cylinder pile sections in 4.88m and 2.44m lengths. Piles were then assembled by joining the precast units end to end. Prestressing obtained 40 kg/cm^2 (figs. 60 and 61). A plastic bonding agent (polyester) seals the joints. Spinning allowed the water/cement ratio to be lowered to 0.29, resulting in a cube strength of about 600 kg/cm^2 after twenty-eight days.

Messrs Heerema cast piles in full length in 220m to 250m long prestressing beds (fig. 62). Inside form panels were segmental steel plates kept distant from each other by ductubes. Spacer bolts kept the inside form panels in place, so that the pile wall was of uniform thickness (figs. 63 and 64).

Fig. 65   The piles for piers 1, 2, and 3 were driven by a 6-ton hammer rig placed on a fill. A water jet of 284 psi churned up the sand along the tip of the pile

Stripping proceeded six hours after concreting, and 24 hours later the tensioning force was transmitted to the concrete. The cement factor was 500 kg per 1m³ of concrete and the water/cement ratio 0.35, so that a cube strength of 600 kg/cm² pas obtained after twenty-eight days.

Pile Driving
Since the lake is shallow from pier 1 to 13, horizontally acting forces can be absorbed solely by vertical driven piles. Because of the numerous iron oxyde layers of the sandy subsoil, jetting had to be used (figs. 65 and 66).

Fig. 66   The concrete piles for piers 4 to 13 inclusive were driven by a 10-ton hammer floating rig and jetting

Fig. 67   Dynamic sounding rod

With a view to determining the depth to which the foundation piles for the bridge piers should be driven Messrs Heerema developed a dynamic sounding rod (figs. 67 and 68). The conical drive point was hydraulically driven, and, after 3cm of penetration, pulled a pipe along with it, so that point pressure was measured first and then the skin friction.

This penetrometer was driven in increments of 30cm. The following were determined at each increment: —

1. Number of blows per 10cm penetration.
2. Point pressure in kg/cm².
3. Skin friction in kg/cm².

The curve for the penetration resistance of the pile is about one metre above the corresponding values of point pressure and skin friction, since the penetration resistance did not become effective before the full cross-section of the 16 in. pile, beginning 1.0m above the pile point, entered the ground (fig. 68).

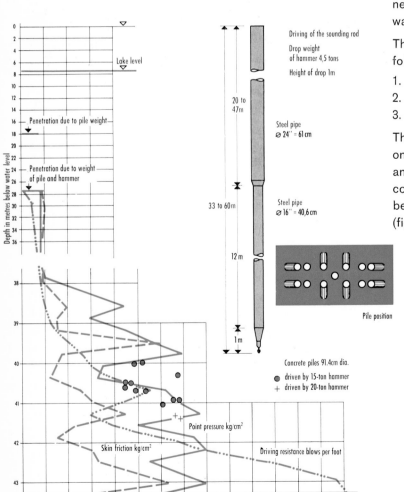

Driving of the sounding rod

Drop weight of hammer 4,5 tons

Height of drop 1m

20 to 47m

Steel pipe ⌀ 24" = 61 cm

33 to 60m

Steel pipe ⌀ 16" = 40,6 cm

12 m

Pile position

1 m

Concrete piles 91.4cm dia.
● driven by 15-ton hammer
+ driven by 20-ton hammer

Fig. 68   Dynamic sounding rod measures driving resistance, point pressure and skin friction at pier 98

Fig. 69   Semi-automatic 20-ton steam hammer at work

The pile lengths were primarily determined by point pressure. As a rule, the reinforced concrete piles could be driven to a depth where the conical drive point of the dynamic sounding rod attained 100 kg/cm². This corresponds to the diagram of Prof. Kérisel, according to which 100 kg/cm² of a sounding rod of 40mm dia. correspond to 70 kg/cm² for a pile of 1.0m dia (fig. 54). A point resistance of 70 kg/cm² and the skin friction result in an ultimate load-bearing capacity of 600 tons for such driven piles.

The batter piles of piers 14 to 19 with a batter of up to 6:1 were driven by a 15-ton hammer to a maximum penetration of 5cm for the last 100 blows.

Driven piles up to 60m and 48 tons were used for the foundations of piers 84 to 104. Messrs Menck & Hambrock, Hamburg, built, as an innovation, a 20-ton semi-automatic steam hammer (fig. 69). Absolute concentricity was a prerequisite to exact driving. The driving cap, loosely placed on the pile head, had to be completely symmetrical for this reason. The pile was guided by a claw, which was not accelerated by the hammer blow.

Comparative test driving made in several piers proved that for a final penetration of 5cm, 100 blows with the 15-ton hammer corresponded to only 10 to 13 blows with the 20-ton hammer (fig. 68). This result agrees well with computations according to the classical and other pile driving formulae.

41

Fig. 70 Pontoon piling plant with 20-ton hammer for driving piles of about 60m in length

Messrs Heerema built a pontoon piling plant for this 20-ton hammer. The leaders consisted of two double T-girders 85cm deep. This pontoon plant handled about 60m long piles weighing about 50 tons (figs. 70 and 71). Up to eight piles in one shift were driven by this floating pile driving plant.

Pile locations were determined by levels and tapes working from the steel towers which had been used for the exploration borings. Practically all piles were placed within 20cm of their exact position. Each pile was carefully examined after driving.

In spite of the hard driving, only about 2 per cent of the piles showed damage, which had to be repaired or made the replacement of a pile necessary.

At the request of the employer, all hollow piles were filled with concrete after driving with a view to improving corrosion resistance.

A total of 634 piles 50 × 50cm totalling 6,260m and a total of 788 piles of 91.4cm dia. totalling 27,400m were driven.

Fig. 71 Handling a 60m long pile

Fig. 72   The "Elephant" working platform and the piling site for a pier
of the big central spans

Fig. 73   The pile-casting yard

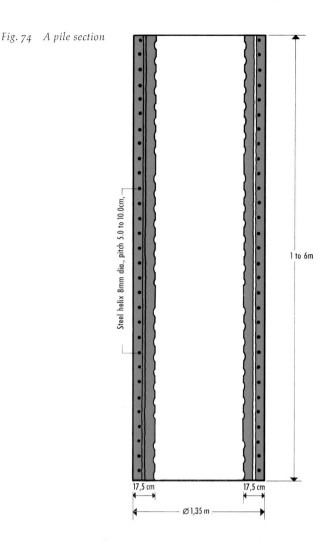

Fig. 74   A pile section

Steel helix 8mm dia., pitch 5.0 to 10.0cm,

1 to 6m

17,5 cm   17,5 cm

∅ 1,35 m

712 piles placed in pre-drilled holes with a total length of 36,256m had to be fabricated for the foundations of the bridge piers. The piles with a length up to 57.5m and 110 tons weight, 135cm dia., were placed by large floating cranes as one unit in the pre-drilled holes.

While beeing hoisted and, subsequently, incorporated in the structure, the piles were subject to bending stresses and had therefore to be prestressed. The concrete had a cube strength of 550 kg/cm². It had to be very dense and sufficiently thick to provide adequate cover for the reinforcement to protect it from the aggressive lake water.

The drilled-hole piles were fabricated in sections 1 to 6m in length, and then joined and tensioned to make piles of the required lengths. This method of fabrication had several advantages. A stock of these sections was fabricated and kept in storage before the exact lengths of the piles were known. They were stored upright and thus required very little yard space (figs. 73 and 74). These piles were well cured before they came in touch with the aggressive water of the lake. At the request of the piling teams, piles of any desired length were assembled from the well seasoned sections within two days. Then the necessary installation for skin and point grouting was mounted (fig. 75).

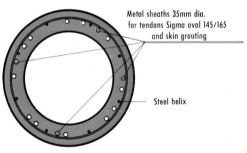

Metal sheaths 35mm dia. for tendons Sigma oval 145/165 and skin grouting

Steel helix

Fig. 75   Skin and point grouting equipment at bottom of drilled-hole pile

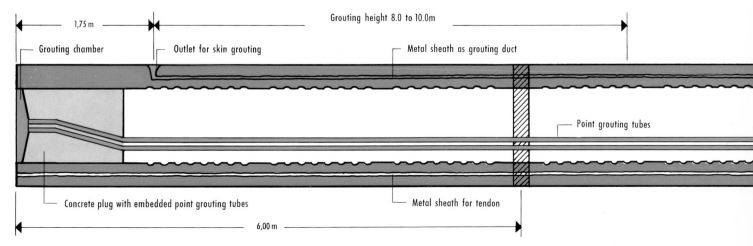

1,75 m

Grouting height 8.0 to 10.0m

Grouting chamber

Outlet for skin grouting

Metal sheath as grouting duct

Point grouting tubes

Concrete plug with embedded point grouting tubes

Metal sheath for tendon

6,00 m

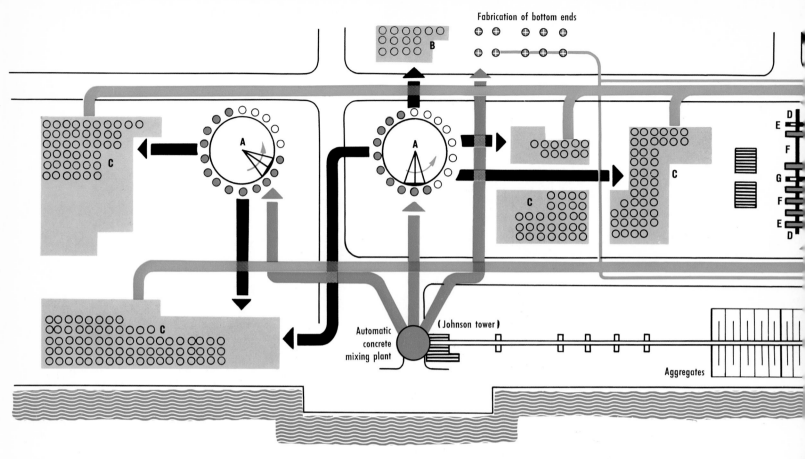

Fabrication of bottom ends

Fig. 76   Pile yard. Flow diagram

■ Concrete transport
■ Transport of sections to storage area
■ Transport of sections to prestressing bed

A Manufacture of sections
B Manufacture of grouting chambers
C Storage yard
D Frames for sections
E Straightening and prestressing bed
F Yard for installation of grouting tubes and grouting
G Handling completed piles
H Storage yard
I Placing of pile bolts
K Barge-loading slip
L Pile barge

A pile yard was installed for producing the sections — 6,314 in all — and assembling the piles (fig. 76). Concrete was mixed in a Johnson tower and transported in agitators to the forms where it was placed by two slewing cranes. Each crane was surrounded by 18 circular bases, upon which the steel vacuum shuttering was installed (fig. 77).

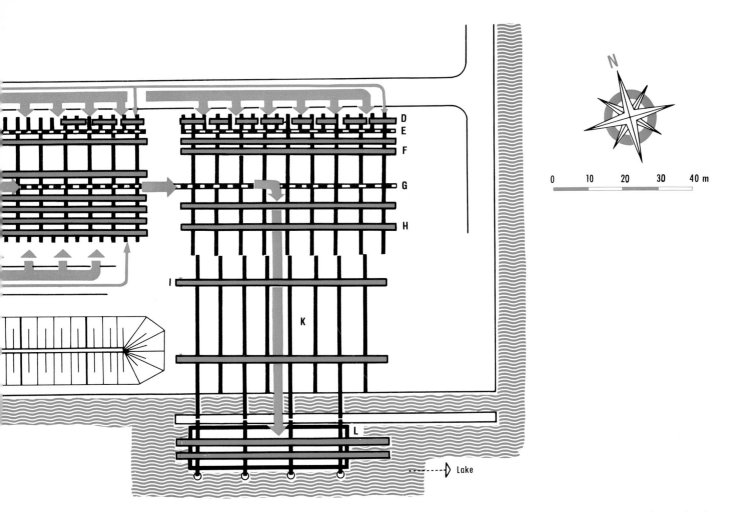

D
E
F
G
H
I
K
L

Lake

N

0   10   20   30   40 m

Fig. 77   Concreting of pile sections arranged around a slewing crane

Fig. 78 Section through vacuum shuttering

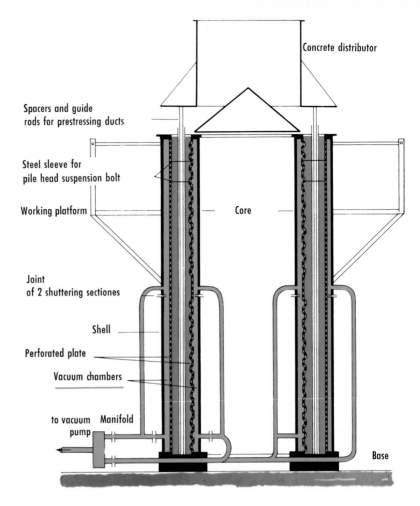

Concrete distributor

Spacers and guide
rods for prestressing ducts

Steel sleeve for
pile head suspension bolt

Working platform

Core

Joint
of 2 shuttering sectiones

Shell

Perforated plate

Vacuum chambers

to vacuum   Manifold
pump

Base

Fig. 79 Slewing crane places corrugated and
perforated interior shuttering

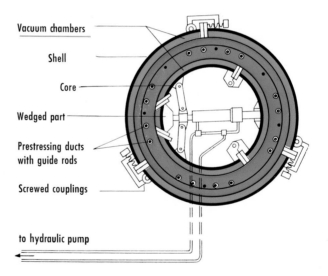

Vacuum chambers

Shell

Core

Wedged part

Prestressing ducts
with guide rods

Screwed couplings

to hydraulic pump

The vacuum concrete method was used for rapid production
and high quality.

The vacuum forms consisted of a shell and a core (fig. 78).
Both had an inner and outer ring with the vacuum chambers
between. These chambers were connected to a vacuum pump
through hoses and a manifold. For concreting, three hinged
segments and the wedged part were spread by rams and
collapsed for stripping.

Fig. 80   The core is covered with a filter cloth, reinforcement and metal sheaths erected, and a workman hangs the filter cloth for the shell on the upper shuttering. The shell is lowered and held firm by screwed couplings. Vacuum hoses can be seen on the shuttering at left

The perforated outer ring of the core was corrugated, thus producing a corrugated inner pile face, which helped to produce a rigid bond between pile concrete and concrete filling.

The shell also consisted of three segments joined by ball and socket-clamps and screwed couplings. Brackets for external vibrators were welded to the outside of the shell. The perforated plates of core and shell were covered with filter cloths before concreting (fig. 80).

The concrete was poured from skips, compacted by external vibrators, and subjected to a vacuum of 7 psi for fifteen to thirty minutes. Within one hour after concreting, the guide rods for the metal sheaths in the pile walls were removed, the section stripped, and sixteen hours later transported to the storage yard. The bottom sections were fitted with a concrete plug containing the star-shaped grouting chamber.

Fig. 81 Pile section is handled by special equipment

The pile sections, weighing up to 15 tons, were handled by special equipment which could pick up, turn, and stack them, and subsequently transport them to the prestressing beds, where they were rolled on to small carriages which moved lengthwise (figs. 81 and 82). These carriages were fitted with rollers which enabled the sections to be rotated until the prestressing ducts were in line. Ductubes were then placed in the prestressing ducts and inflated so that the ducts were kept open when the sections were joined.

The piles were prestressed on the Holzmann KA System, which uses oval-ribbed steel having 145 to 160 kg/m² ultimate strength. The prestressing force was large enough to prevent tensional stresses in the piles phen being hoisted in a triple sling (fig. 84). The total prestressing force per pile amounted ot 260 to 380 tons.

Numerous tests were necessary to find the most suitable composition of grout for injection into the prestressing ducts. Owing to the high ambient temperatures, the prefabricated members became so hot that there was some danger of clogging in the 60m long ducts. Under these conditions, the best grout was found to have a water/cement ratio of 0.42. An addition of 0.27 per cent No. 8 Pozzolith was found to be advantageous.

After prestressing, the piles were rolled on to a bed consisting of beams, where the ducts were grouted, the anchorage system removed, and the pipes for skin and point grouting installed (fig. 83).

Before transporting each pile to the site, its pipe system was subjected to a hydraulic test, since the load-bearing capacity depended on the quality and workmanship of skin and point grouting.

Fig. 82 Joining and placing piles on barge

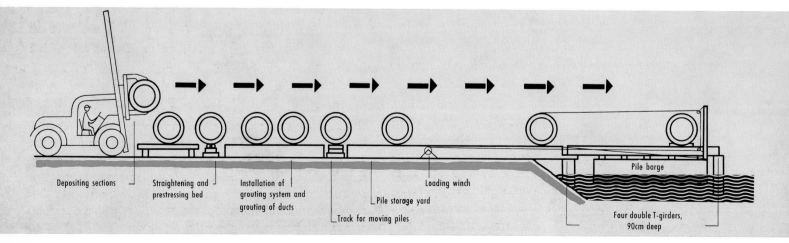

Depositing sections | Straightening and prestressing bed | Installation of grouting system and grouting of ducts | Track for moving piles | Pile storage yard | Loading winch | Pile barge | Four double T-girders, 90cm deep

1 Anchorage system
2 Grouted ducts
3 Ducts for skin grouting
4 Pipes for point grouting

Fig. 83   The left pile is tensioned and the metal sheaths are grouted. The tensioning frames are removed on the next pile and the projecting prestressing reinforcement cut off the right pile

Fig. 84   Prestressing drilled-hole piles

Two 900-ton deck barges were fitted for transporting the piles (fig. 85). Four double T-girders, 90cm deep, were mounted in such a way that, on flooding the barge, the landside ends rested on the loading installation and the lake ends on dolphins. This precluded the barges' moving when the piles were rolled on.

Every week, up to 16 piles could be fabricated, transported, and placed.

Pile weight in tons

| | 8 × 8 38,5 kg/cm² | 10 × 8 48,5 kg/cm² | 12 × 8 .... 58,2 kg/cm² | Number of tendons. Compressive stress of concrete subjected to prestress |

100
90
80
70
60

35   40   45   50   55   60
Pile length in metres

Fig. 85   Piles on the deck barge. The head bolts are set at an angle of 90° to each other

Fig. 86 The "Giraffe" floating crane places a 57.5m pile. Drilling equipment can be seen at work on the "Elephant" platform

Drilling Holes and Placing Piles

To transmit the unusually heavy bridge loads to deeper soil trata of sufficient bearing capacity, drilled-hole piles 50m to 60m in length and with 500 ton to 700 ton load-bearing capacity were necessary (fig. 86).

Two thirds of the total load of the bridge was founded on drilled-hole piles, the remainder on driven piles.

Drilling

Only a continuous process would have been fast enough and sufficiently economical to drill 25,704 linear metres in soil in the allotted time. The successful Salzgitter Maschinen A. G. reverse circulation drilling method was therefore used. This method employs equipment which cuts into the soil with a bit, the drillings being conveyed to the surface through the hollow drilling rods by a suction pump. The water sucked to the surface is replaced by filling water (fig. 87). When employing this method for well sinking, the boreholes are generally not cased or cased only in their upper part, since the filling water pressure prevents cave-ins.

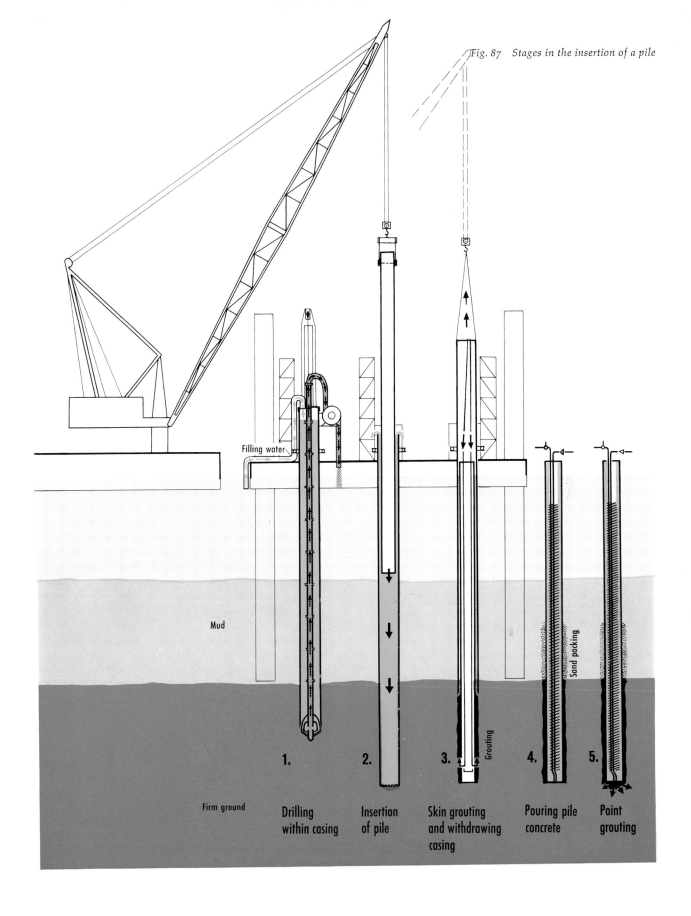

Fig. 87 Stages in the insertion of a pile

Filling water

Mud

Firm ground

1.	2.	3.	4.	5.
Drilling within casing	Insertion of pile	Skin grouting and withdrawing casing	Pouring pile concrete	Point grouting

Sand packing

Grouting

This simple procedure could not be employed in this instance because the boreholes collapsed if the piles were not inserted into the holes immediately after drilling. The piles, while being inserted, could also damage the unprotected walls of the boreholes and would then rest on loose soil. The boreholes were therefore fully cased. The rigs for running and withdrawing the casing were supplied by Messrs. Bade of Lehrte, Germany (fig. 88).

A hydraulically operated rotary table was placed on the casing and rotated the drill pipe and the bit. The hollow drill pipe was connected by a hose to a scution pump which sucked the drillings to the surface. A pump kept the water level within the casing at 1m below the top of the casing. This excess water pressure in the casing had to be maintained until the pile was inserted, to prevent the soil from caving in at the bottom of the hole.

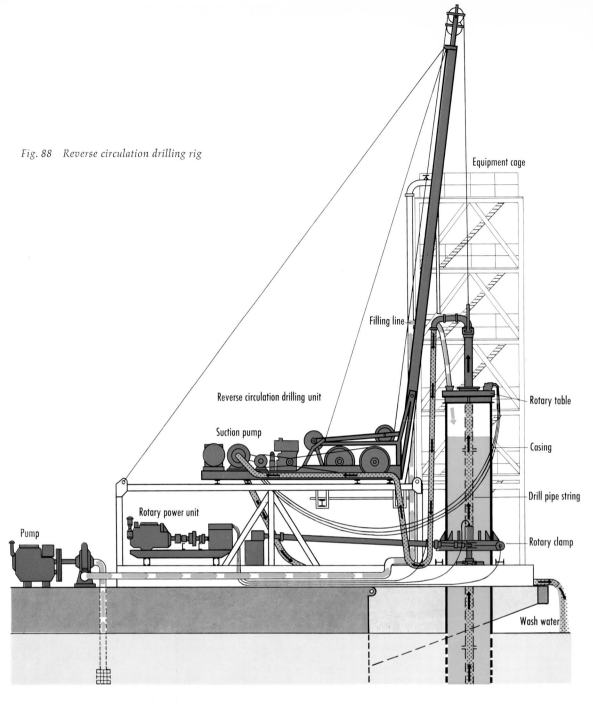

Fig. 88   Reverse circulation drilling rig

Equipment cage

Filling line

Reverse circulation drilling unit

Suction pump

Rotary table

Casing

Rotary power unit

Drill pipe string

Pump

Rotary clamp

Wash water

Side view

Fig. 89   *Cage with reverse circulation drilling unit and rotary power unit*

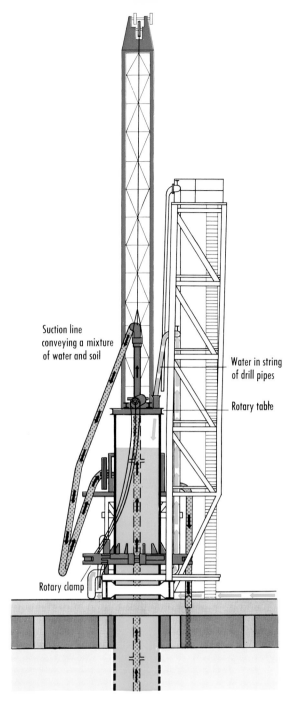

Suction line
conveying a mixture
of water and soil

Water in string
of drill pipes

Rotary table

Rotary clamp

Front view

The drill string consisted of pipes 3m long screwed together, and the casing of 10m welded sections.

The reverse circulation drilling unit and the rotary power unit were mounted in a cage which a crane could place wherever required for drilling (fig. 89). The cage, including equipment, weighed 45 tons.

Great difficulty was encountered in designing a bit capable of handling all types of soil encountered at the bridge site. It had to penetrate mud, sand, silt, conglomerate, and sandstone, and the suction ports had to resist clogging by tough clay. The result of many experiments showed the best solution to be a four-way bit whose teeth were staggered so that two consecutive wings attacked the whole bottom of the borehole.

Drilling progress varied considerably in the different types of soil. The net drilling time, excluding the time required for the addition of drill pipes or casing sections, was

in mud 1.0 to 2.5 m/h
in sand mixed with clay or silt, and conglomerates 0.5 to 1.5 m/h
in sand alone 1.5 to 3.0 m/h.

The average drilling progress for a whole pile, including all ancillary work, amounted to:

Piers 20 to 27 0.84m/h in sand and a great deal of conglomerate,
Piers 28 to 37 1.26m/h in sand interspersed with clay and layers of sandstone,
Piers 61 to 81 2.03m/h in almost exclusively sand.

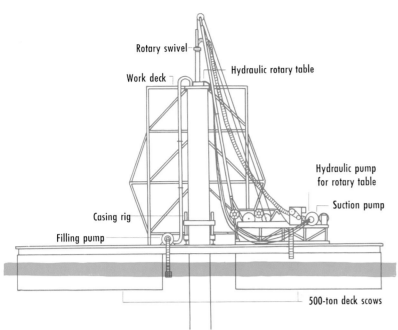

Rotary swivel

Work deck

Hydraulic rotary table

Hydraulic pump
for rotary table

Suction pump

Casing rig

Filling pump

500-ton deck scows

Fig. 90 Floating drilling rig

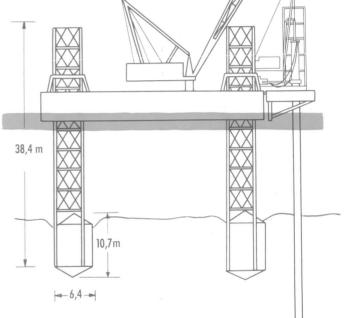

Fig. 91 Barge "Elephant"

38,4 m

10,7m

6,4

Fig. 92 Barges "Coche" and "Cubagua"

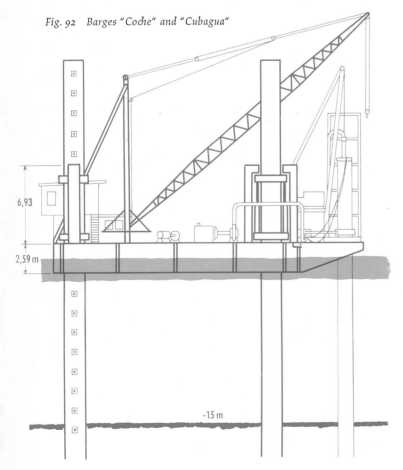

6,93

2,59 m

-15 m

In the beginning, floating equipment was used, and rendered good service under shelter from the shore, so long as water depths averaged about 10m (fig. 90). For deeper water, how-ever — so as to preclude interference from wind and waves — three working barges were employed. The largest barge, the "Elephant" had a triangular platform, each side being 40m long, and three caissons. A crane was mounted on the barge (fig. 91). Attached to one side was a hinged secondary plat-form, 7.30m wide, carrying the drilling rig. Racks were fitted to the three edges of each caisson; and three mechanisms to raise and lower the platform were geared to each rack; i. e. nine mechanisms to each caisson. The crane had a main block lifting capacity of 225 tons at 62m hook height above the platform and an auxiliary block having a 91-ton lifting capacity at 64m hook height. This working barge was also used for various other kinds of work at the bridge site.

The other working barges, the "Coche" and "Cubagua", had 24.4m by 22.6m platforms with a hinged secondary platform 6m wide for the drilling equipment (fig. 92).

The four caissons of each working barge consisted of 1.83m dia. steel tubes 48m long, which were raised and lowered by jacks. The smaller working barges carried 12-ton derricks. A floating crane, the "Giraffe", having a main block of 125-ton capacity at 76m hook height above the platform, and a secondary block having a 10-ton capacity at 80m hook height was available for handling heavier loads such as cages with drilling equipment, piles, etc.

Lifting and inserting the piles up to 57.5m long and 110 tons in weight proved very difficult, especially when it was windy. Piles were slung at three points, the main block being connected to a head bolt (fig. 93).

Fig. 93   The "Elephant" working barge handling a pile slung at three points

Fig. 94 Inserting a pile
1. Two scows ready to skin-grout
2. Scow for point pressure-grouting point-grouts piles inserted 5 days previously and filled with concrete

Skin Grouting

While withdrawing the casing, the annulus of 7.5cm between the casing and the pile was pressure-grouted in firm soil, thus producing a firm bond between the pile and the soil (fig. 87). For skin grouting, two deck scows were used, each of which could mix and handle 3 to 4m³ of grout per hour. These deck scows were equipped with storage sheds for 4,000 bags of cement, rooms for personnel, tool stores, generators, air compressors, hydraulic pumps, a mixing plant, and three boojee pumps (or grouting machines) (fig. 94).

The grout was forced from above through hoses into grouting lines in the pipe wall (figs. 74 and 75) and egressed from these lines at the bottom between pile and casing (fig. 87).

While the casing was being withdrawn, the level of grout was always kept one metre above the bottom of the casing to ensure that no soil could enter the annulus between pile and casing. Grouting was restricted to firm soil. For the following 5m above the latter, the annular space between pile and mud was filled with sand to keep the pile steady until the grout had hardened.

Pouring Concrete into the Hollow Piles

The hollow piles were filled with concrete to enable them to take up the bending moments resulting from the horizontal forces originating in the superstructure.

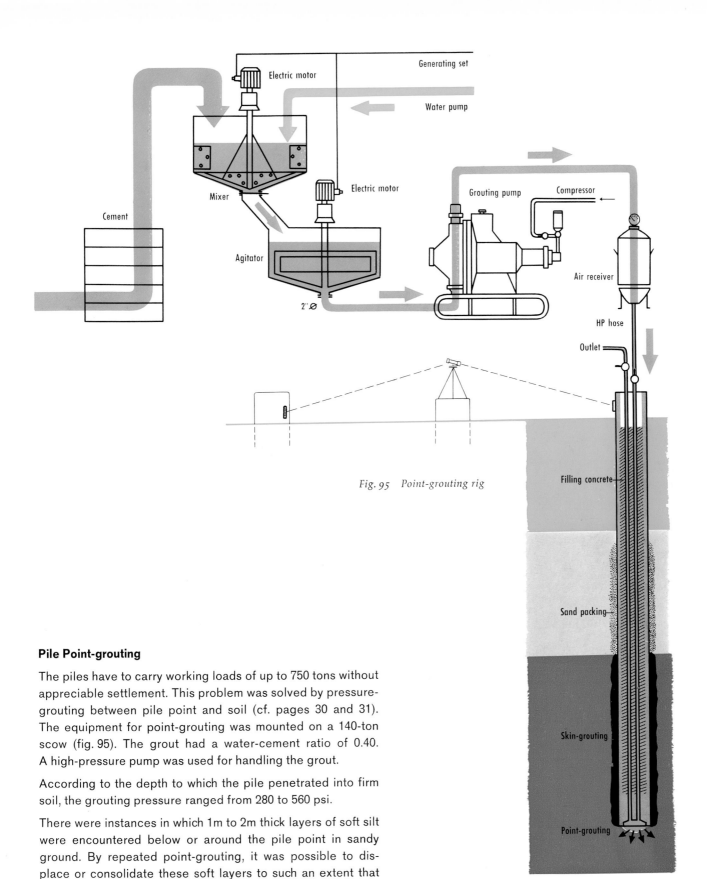

Fig. 95   Point-grouting rig

Electric motor

Generating set

Water pump

Grouting pump

Compressor

Electric motor

Air receiver

Mixer

Cement

Agitator

2" ∅

HP hose

Outlet

Filling concrete

Sand packing

Skin-grouting

Point-grouting

Pile Point-grouting

The piles have to carry working loads of up to 750 tons without appreciable settlement. This problem was solved by pressure-grouting between pile point and soil (cf. pages 30 and 31). The equipment for point-grouting was mounted on a 140-ton scow (fig. 95). The grout had a water-cement ratio of 0.40. A high-pressure pump was used for handling the grout.

According to the depth to which the pile penetrated into firm soil, the grouting pressure ranged from 280 to 560 psi.

There were instances in which 1m to 2m thick layers of soft silt were encountered below or around the pile point in sandy ground. By repeated point-grouting, it was possible to displace or consolidate these soft layers to such an extent that later load tests on these piles gave excellent results. While for most piles 150 to 300 litres of grout were used, these piles required up to 3,000 litres of grout.

Especially under the central piers, the subsoil varied considerably as a result of which, to attain an equal point resistance, the amount of grout to be injected also varied considerably. By ensuring equal point resistance for all the piles of one pier, the varying properties of the different types of soil were successfully equalized and a differential settlement precluded.

59

Design and Execution of Superstructure

Fig. 96 *Constructing 235m spans*

Fig. 97   The "Ajax" 250-ton floating crane handles 46.60m long precast girders

Spans of 36.60m and 46.60m

About half the bridge length consists of span of 36.60m and 46.60m. In this section of 4.435m, operations went on simultaneously for piles, pile caps, piers, and precast girders (fig. 98). All these operations depended on the progress of the foundation work, which was hard to foresee and full of surprises. The problems in this section were therefore primarily organisational.

Fig. 98 Constructing 46.60m spans. In the background, placed precast girders are transversely prestressed; at centre, a pile driver ready for work and a pile cap beeing concreted; in the foreground, a twin scow floats prefabricated shuttering into position

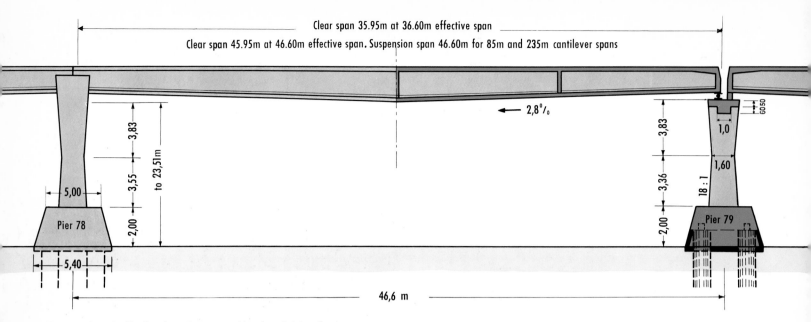

Clear span 35.95m at 36.60m effective span

Clear span 45.95m at 46.60m effective span. Suspension span 46.60m for 85m and 235m cantilever spans

← 2,8%

Fig. 99 Longitudinal and transverse section of a 46.60m effective span

The 36.60m and 46.60m spans are of similiar type (fig. 99). The foundation piles are capped by a pile cap in which the four reinforced concrete walls of a pier are held. At the top the pier walls are joined by a tee-section transverse concrete girder 1.1m deep. This girder supports the deck spans which are formed by four prefabricated tee-section girders spaced at centre distances of 4.50m (fig. 99). These prefabricated tee-section girders differ only in length and depth. With only slight changes, both types of girder could therefore be cast in the same moulds. The tee-section girders have thickened bases the bottoms of which are inclined by 2.8 per cent in longitudinal direction (fig. 99).

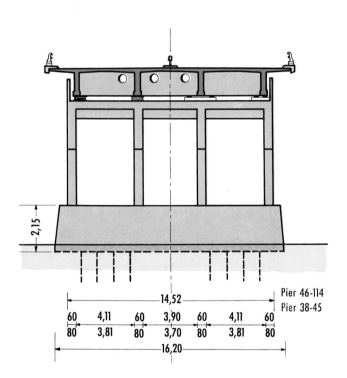

Pier 46-114
Pier 38-45

Pile Caps (Heavy Concrete Slabs)

Wave action precluded the shuttering for the pile caps to be erected in-situ. It was therefore decided to cast reinforced concrete shuttering units on the shore. These units, which were fastened to the pile heads, served as working platforms at the same time. They incorporated part of the reinforcement required for the heavy concrete slabs.

Before casting any reinforced concrete shuttering unit on land, the pile locations of the respective group were checked, so as to ensure that the holes in the bottom of the unit were correctly positioned (fig. 100).

An electric gantry lifted the units, weighing 75 tons, on a steel spreader bar and carried them to the loading quay. Here, they were transferred, together with the steel spreader bar to one of the jibs (cantilever arms) of the twin scow (fig. 101). This twin scow was also used for placing the suspended spans.

The twin scow was then tugged to the pile group. Here it was flooded until the distance between the pile heads and the shuttering unit had been reduced to 10cm. Jacks installed under the jib (cantilever arm) were then lowered quickly, so that repeated up and down movement due to wave action was avoided.

Fig. 100 *Preparing reinforcement with tie wire for a reinforced concrete shuttering unit for 46.60m spans*

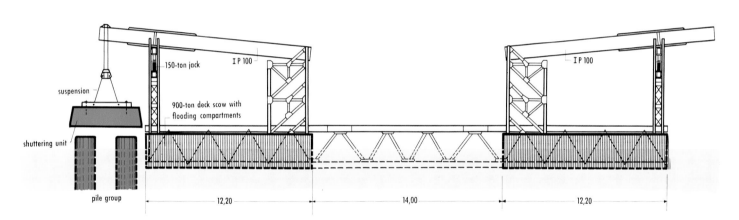

Fig. 101 *Twin scow places reinforced concrete shuttering unit on pile group*

Further operations were: —

Pumping out the hollow piles whenever they had been filled with water.

Placing projecting reinforcement to marry the pile to the pile cap.

Placing pile cap reinforcement and projecting reinforcement for the pier walls.

Placing shuttering for the pile caps.

Pouring 4,266-psi concrete (B 350).

Reinforced Concrete Pier Walls and Tee-section Transverse Concrete Girders

Steel shuttering was used for concreting the pier walls of the 46.60m spans. The first shuttering climbed up to the "waist", and the second one served for the upper part of the pier wall and the tee-section transverse concrete girder. The shuttering sets were assembled on the shore. Handling was by floating cranes. Reinforcing cages were also assembled on land and placed by floating cranes, which also transferred the concrete from floating mixing plants to the steel shuttering.

Precast Prestressed Girders

The bridge has a total of 528 precast, prestressed girders, i. e. 5,928.4m or 72 per cent of the bridge length consists of prefabricated girders. The wide use made of standardisation and prefabrication has greatly contributed to the speed of constrction. The 36.60m spans are bridged directly with 80 girders and the 46.60m spans are bridged directly with 308 girders while in the case of the longer spans (85m and 235m) 140 girders are suspended between cantilever sections resting on the piers. The reinforcing cage for a girder, together with the tendons and anchor plates, was assembled on large wooden supports and then placed with a steel spreader bar by the electric gantry in the steel mould (fig. 102).

The concrete foundations for the steel mould had the same inclination as the bottom of the girders. The sides of the mould were moved on rails (fig. 103). During concreting, the two halves of the mould were held together by rag bolts. The shuttering for the prefabricated bridge deck was readjusted by set screws before any pour of concrete and lowered again for stripping.

Fig. 102   Electric gantry placing reinforcing cage in mould

Fig. 103   Reinforcing cage on bottom of mould — sides being prepared for positioning

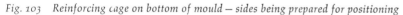

Concrete was brought by truck mixers of 3.0m³ capacity, placed by truck cranes with concrete skips, and compacted by internal and external vibrators. The deck was smoothed by a vibrating screed.

The girders were made of 6,399-psi concrete (B 450).

For prestressing, use was made of the Morandi System (fig. 104). The cables consist of multiples of three wires, as the wires are anchored in groups of three.

The main and cross girders are prestressed with tendons consisting of eighteen cold-drawn wires of 7mm dia. held by six conical anchors. Each conical anchor has three grooves. Wires are of basic Siemens-Martin steel with 0.8 per cent carbon; having 150 kg to 170 kg/mm² ultimate strength.

After the 36.60m girders had been made, there was no difficulty in remodelling the moulds for the 46.60m girders. There were six moulds in which six girders could be produced in one week. The electric gantry transported the girders to the storage yard (fig. 105).

Fig. 104   Prestressing a girder

Fig. 105   Girders stored in three tiers

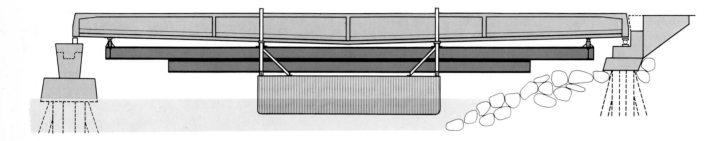

Fig. 106 Floating a 36.60m girder into position by 900=ton scow

Fig. 107 Electric gantry transfers a 46.60m girder to a twin scow

Fig. 108   Towing twin scow into position

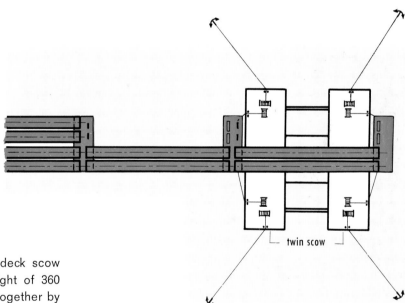

twin scow

Fig. 109   Twin scow being correctly positioned by winches to enable the girders to be placed directly on the bearings

Floating Girders Into Position

The 36.60m girders were handled by a 900-ton deck scow (fig. 106). For two 46.60m girders of a total weight of 360 tons, two scows were necessary; they were tied together by lattice girders. This twin scow carried two steel placing scaffolds which could be adjusted to each pier height. A cantilever steel arm with hydraulic mechanism for raising and lowering was mounted on each placing scaffold. These arms carried the girders (fig. 108).

The twin scow was towed to the placing site (figs. 108 and 109). Two girders were placed simultaneously, first on the fixed bearings and subsequently on the movable ones, by flooding the compartments of the twin scow and operating the hydraulic mechanisms. Here, the upper plates of the roller bearings were bonded to the girders with a plastic adhesive to eliminate shear. Under favourable weather conditions, two trips could be made per day, and thus four girders placed.

Fig. 110   250-ton "Ajax" floating crane places 190-ton girder into position

Placing 46.60m Spans by Floating Crane

Like the 36.60m spans, the 46.60m spans were also floated to the placing sites by the twin scow, but they were raised by the 250-ton "Ajax" floating crane from the twin scow on to their higher supports (fig. 110). Since the girders could not take up the axial stress which would result from a simple rigging, they were lifted by means of a steel spreader bar. A girder was first placed on the centre pin of the fixed bearing which gave it guidance, and was then pulled by rope pulley blocks transversely to the bridge axis to its correct position on the movable bearing. Here also, with favorable weather and in calm water, up to four girders could be placed per day.

Girder Bearings

Steel-sheathed concrete roller bearings on the Burkhardt System were used for movable bearings which were dimensioned for a Hertzian pressure of 4.0 tons/cm², assuming a modulus of elasticity of 400,000 kg/cm² (fig. 111). For the design of the bearing plates parabolic stress distribution was assumed, and concrete pressures up to 200 kg/cm² were allowed for.

The manufacturers of the bearings, Maschinenfabrik Eßlingen, Germany, carried out tests to obtain detailed information on the value of rolling friction under high Hertzian pressure (fig. 112). The force necessary to move a plate between the rollers at a rate of 0.11 mm/sec under Hertzian pressures of 3.2, 3.5, and 4.3 ton/cm² was measured. The values for rolling friction proved to be considerably below 1 per cent of the surcharge, and therefore well below the assumed value of 3 per cent.

Tests for a comparison between steel-sheathed concrete rollers and rollers made of 52 grade steel proved that the concrete rollers, owing to their higher elasticity, show less plastic deformation, and therefore less roller friction too (fig. 112).

As protection against corrosion, 0.3 per cent copper was added to the steel of the tubes and bearing plates; they were sandblasted, metallized by spraying them with aluminium, and finally dressed with two coats of chlorinated rubber paint.

The fixed bearings consist of 2cm thick lead plates with steel centre pins 5cm in dia.

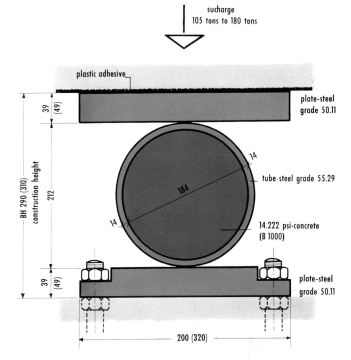

Fig. 111 *Burkhardt roller bearings — dimensions in mm. The bracketed dimensions apply to the 46.60m girders*

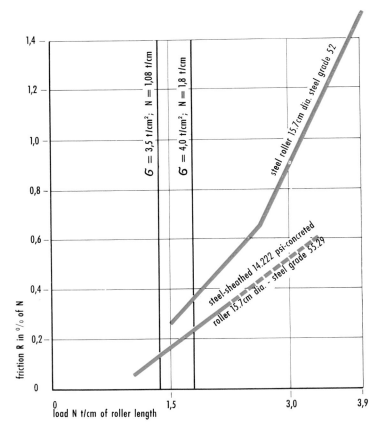

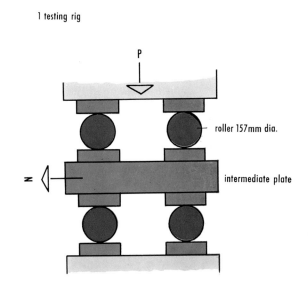

Fig. 112 *Friction set up by steel-sheathed concrete and steel rollers was determined by experiment*

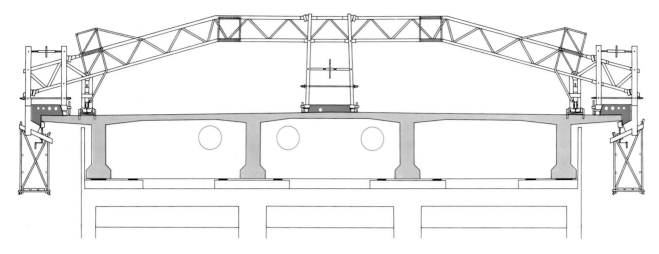

Fig. 113   Travelling shuttering rig used in concreting the central reserve and the two sidewalks

Construction

After the girders had been placed, tendons on the Morandi System were inserted in the sheet-metal sheaths of the prefabricated deck and the ribs. Then the joints between the girders were filled with concrete, and finally the deck was prestressed transversely to the axis of the bridge.

Four travelling shuttering rigs, each 11.7m long, were used. The lattice girders of these rigs were raised in the centre to allow site traffic to pass underneath (figs. 113 and 114). The railings are aluminium and were built in accordance with ASTM Standard Specifications. Guide rails are installed all along the central reserve.

Fig. 114   Concreting the central reserve and the two sidewalks

85m Spans

Fig. 115   Trestle pier 19 towers 49.50m into the sky

The 85m spans are the approach spans for the five 235m spans over the shipping channel. The sixteen trestle piers on the western side have heights between 18.90m and 49.50m and the twelve trestle piers on the eastern side are between 27.30m and 49.50m high. The total length of the 85m spans is 2,426m, or nearly 30 per cent of the length of the bridge.

The deck of the 85m spans has a gradient of 2.47 per cent, which means that each trestle pier is 2.04m higher than the previous one. For obtaining the necessary height increase, the reinforced concrete pier walls were lengthened in their lower parts. In this way, the V-shape of pier 8 changed gradually, with increasing height, to the slender H-shape of the highest trestle piers, 19 and 26 (fig. 115).

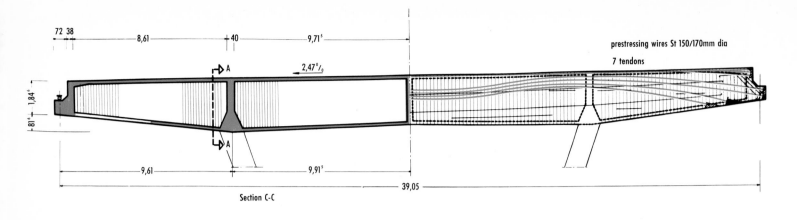

Section C-C

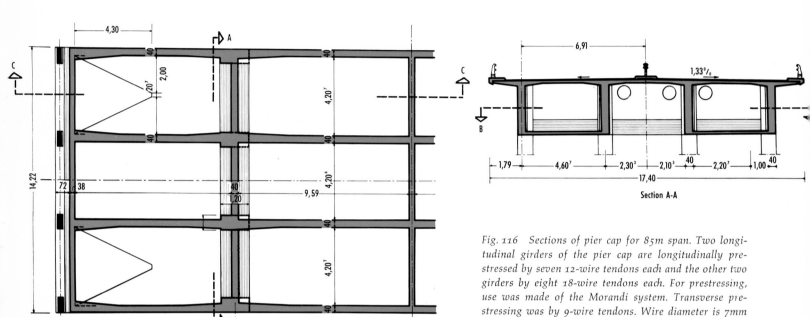

Section B-B

Section A-A

Fig. 116   Sections of pier cap for 85m span. Two longitudinal girders of the pier cap are longitudinally prestressed by seven 12-wire tendons each and the other two girders by eight 18-wire tendons each. For prestressing, use was made of the Morandi system. Transverse prestressing was by 9-wire tendons. Wire diameter is 7mm and the steel has an ultimate strength of 150 kg to 170 kg/mm²

Principles of the Structural Analysis for the 85m Spans

For the analysis of the foundations, piles and pile caps were assumed to be flexurally-rigid frames. Horizontally applied test loads proved that the piles could be regarded as rigidly retained in the ground. Only a few piles in groups 13 to 19 were driven at a rake. In all the other groups, the vertical piles transfer the horizontally acting loads to firm ground. Fibre stresses from prestressing, axial forces and moments attain 150 kg/cm². The piles can take up these fibre stresses without difficulty, since they are made of 7,821-psi concrete (B 550). They are filled with 4,266-psi concrete (B 300). Tensile stresses were not allowed for in the piles.

The "H"-shaped members are frames with a hyperstatic factor of six in the direction of the axis of the bridge. They are flexibly restrained in pile and pier caps. Transversely to the bridge, they also act as frames. They were dimensioned for 4,266-psi concrete (B 300) and reinforcing steel IIa, having a tensile strength of 5,000 to 6,400 kg/cm², in accordance with DIN 1045.

A pier cap consists of two 39.05m long box sections, which tie together in-situ concrete deck and cross beams (fig. 116).

The pier caps are prestressed longitudinally, the deck transversely, and the three innermost cross beams concentrically.

The pier caps were designed as statically determinate girders, since their restraint — bearing in mind the ratio of rigidity of superstructure to "H"-shaped members — was negligible.

Structural analysis was complicated by the continuously changing systems and loads during the different phases of the work.

Pile Caps

Each western pier rests on a pile group composed of eighteen to twenty-four driven piles, 91.4cm in dia., while each pier to the east of the shipping channel spans rests on a pile group composed of ten to sixteen 135cm dia. inserted piles. Contrary to the 46.60m spans, there are two 16m by 4.55m by 2.70m thick pile caps tied together by four heavy reinforced concrete beams. In the same way as for the 46.60m spans, the bottom shuttering was fabricated on shore and placed by floating crane on the pile heads (figs. 117 and 118).

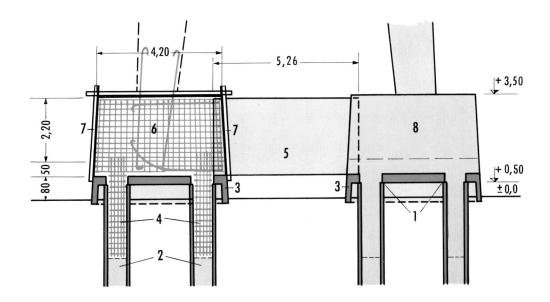

Fig. 117 Diagrammatic Arrangement of Pile Cap Work

1. *Heads of driven piles are cut down at 0.5m above sea level datum and inserted piles at 1.2m above sea level datum*

2. *Hollow piles were pumped out and filled with concrete up to 4.0m below sea level datum*

3. *Prefabricated bottom shuttering was placed on pile heads by floating crane*

4. *The projecting reinforcement was installed and the pile heads were concreted*

5. *The 45-ton reinforced concrete beams were cast on shore and placed by a 60-ton floating crane*

6. *Reinforcement was placed for pile cap and for marrying the legs of the "H"-shaped or "V"-shaped piers to the pile cap*

7. *The aprons of the bottom shuttering were provided with channel irons for guidance and correct retention of side shuttering. Floating cranes placed the 3m by 4m shuttering panels*

8. *Since the bottom shuttering is only 30cm thick, concrete was poured in one 50cm layer and another 220cm layer. Concrete was transferred by belt conveyors from floating mixing plants to the pouring points*

Fig. 118   Floating crane places 75-ton bottom shuttering

Fig. 119   Concreting is completed and the climbing shutters are being raised for the next pour

Reinforced Concrete Pier Walls

When concreting the inclined pier walls and raising the climbing shutters, there was a constant change in the inherent forces which had to be taken into account at all times so as to ensure that the allowable stresses were not exceeded.

For the construction of a trestle pier, four sets of Luchterhand type metal shutters were used, that is, one set of climbing metal shutters for the bottom part and another for the top

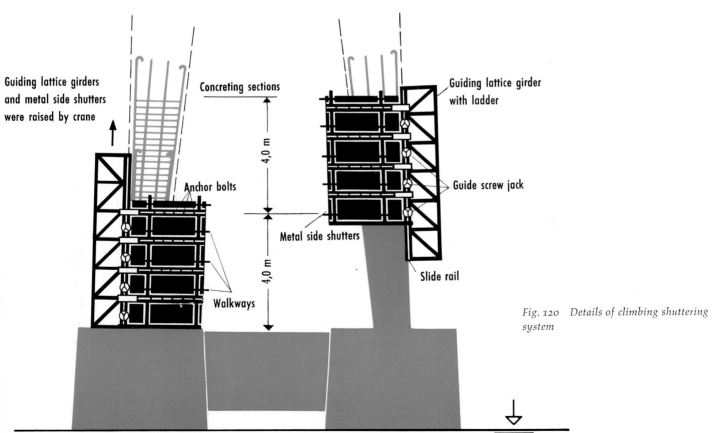

Guiding lattice girders
and metal side shutters
were raised by crane

Concreting sections

Guiding lattice girder
with ladder

4,0 m

Anchor bolts

Guide screw jack

Metal side shutters

4,0 m

Slide rail

Walkways

Fig. 120   Details of climbing shuttering system

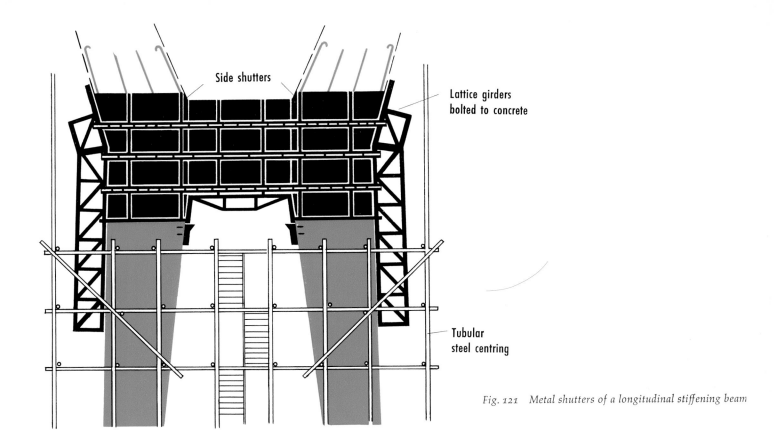

Side shutters

Lattice girders
bolted to concrete

Tubular
steel centring

Fig. 121   Metal shutters of a longitudinal stiffening beam

part of the pier. Thereto, one set of metal shutters for the longitudinal stiffening beams and another for the cross stiffening beams were used (figs. 119 to 123).

The climbing shutters were guided by lattice girders. Together with panels, these girders formed the front shuttering and retained the reinforcement in position. As soon as the lattice girders were firmly bolted to the hardenend reinforced concrete, the side shutters were loosened and raised by a tower crane. This crane was mounted 5m away from the pile

cap on a steel cantilever arm, which, in turn, was fixed to the heavy reinforced concrete beams of the pile cap (figs. 124 and 125).

The reinforcing cages were 8m to 12m high. The concrete was mixed in floating plants and poured in 4m layers. The shutters had to be carefully readjusted before pouring a succeeding layer so as to ensure that at a height of 45m the top of any pier wall would be within 1.5cm of of alignment. It took three days to complete a 4m high section.

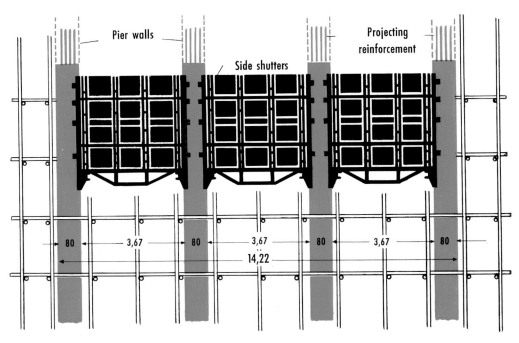

Pier walls

Projecting
reinforcement

Side shutters

80   3,67   80   3,67   80   3,67   80

14,22

*Fig. 122   Metal shutters of a cross
stiffening beam*

Fig. 123   Climbing shuttering for "V"-shaped piers in place

Fig. 124   Concreting pier cap girder

Fig. 125   Longitudinal prestressing of pier cap girder

Fig. 126   *Shuttering and reinforcement for the pier caps are placed on the steel service girders on land*

Pier Caps

Steel service girders were used for the construction of the pier caps so as to avoid vertical falsework. These service girders were placed on the completed pier legs. The superstructure loads were thus transferred to the uncapped system of pier legs. Therefore, horizontal ties were provided temporarily at the bearing areas of the service girders. When lowering the girders, these members were detensioned and removed (fig. 130). The resultant of the superstructure loads and tensioned forces of the ties was allowed only slight deviation from the centre lines of the inclined pier legs. The required stress condition had to be established prior to the completion of the pier cap, since this required a state of stress that could not be obtained after the capping had been completed.

The idea of using the continuously changing static system for absorbing the concreting loads and that of influencing under controlled conditions the deformation and moments of the uncapped pier leg system by the use of auxiliary ties was realized here in a manner hitherto unknown and further developed when constructing the piers for the 235m spans.

This method is somewhat similar to the cantilever method of construction, but it involves greater differences between the static systems during construction and after completion. As always necessary in the case of continuously changing systems and loads during construction, it was also necessary to check that the concrete stresses were redistributed by creep in such a way as to correspond to the support and continuity conditions of the final system.

Preliminary Pier Cap Work on Shore

As far as possible, the pier caps were prepared on shore (fig. 126). Only the cross beams and the deck between the box girders had to be shuttered and reinforced in-situ.

The trussed steel centring for a pier cap consisted of two double lattice girders located below the webs of the box girders. Walkways, railings, scaffoldings and ladders were installed in the service girders on shore. Each half of a service girder weighed 130 tons, including shuttering and reinforcement, and was placed on deck scows by electric gantry (fig. 127).

Fig. 127   Electric gantry transfers steel service girder to deck scow

Fig. 128　The "Ajax" floating crane positions a service girder

Positioning Steel Service Girders

The steel service girders were positioned by floating cranes (figs. 128 and 129). Since there was a gap of only a few centimetres between the girder and pier walls, the positioning made exacting demands on the crane operator and could only be carried out during fine weather. This procedure was successfully performed 56 times in sequence.

Fig. 129   The "Giraffe" 125-ton floating crane places a service girder on one of the two highest piers of the 85mm spans

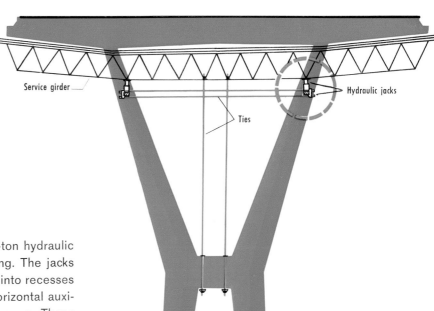

Fig. 130   Hydraulic jacks align service girder. Ties prevent overstressing of pier walls

Each service girder was placed on sixteen 100-ton hydraulic jacks for alignment. It was lowered after pouring. The jacks were mounted on short steel beams which fitted into recesses of the pier legs (figs. 131 and 132). The eight horizontal auxiliary ties were also anchored to these steel beams. These members were 26mm in dia. and the steel had an ultimate strength of 80 to 105 kg/mm².

Concreting the Pier Caps

The service girders had the same statical system as the pier caps, but a less favourable ratio of span. It was therefore necessary to select the concreting sections with this in mind so as to avoid crack formation during concreting through flexure of the service girder.

First, the two cantilever girders were concreted. This lowered by 75mm the extremities of the cantilevers and produced a hog of 17mm of the centre part. Then, the service girder was deflected 14mm in the centre by using vertical ties, thereby anticipating central flexure resulting from concreting (fig. 130). The vertical ties were 26mm in dia. and the steel had an ultimate strength of 80 to 105 kg/mm². When the centre part was being concreted, the vertical ties were detensioned so as to obviate further flexure of the pier cap.

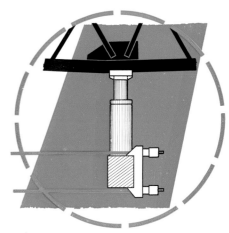

Fig. 131   The second half of a service girder is being placed on jacks

81

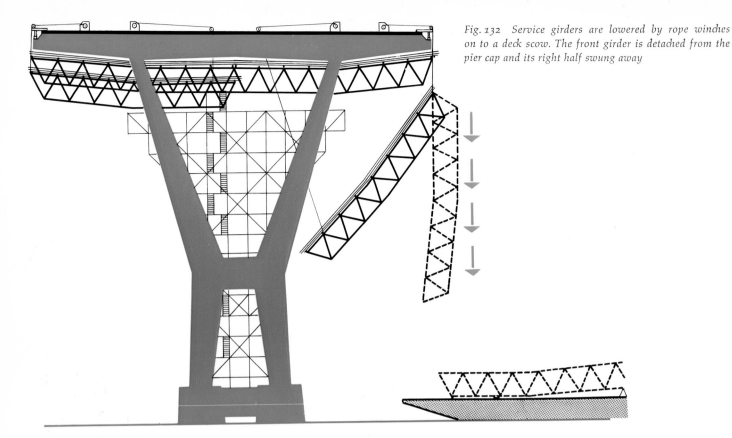

Fig. 132 Service girders are lowered by rope winches on to a deck scow. The front girder is detached from the pier cap and its right half swung away

Removal of Service Girders

After the pier caps had been partially prestressed to about 30 per cent, so as to allow them to carry their own weight, the service girders could be lowered by jacks and the horizontal ties detensioned.

While prestressing, grouting and stripping operations were in progress, the service girders were suspended from rope winches and unbolted in the centre. After removing the jacks, the cross beam shuttering and the upper part of the tubular steel scaffolding, the two halves of the service girder were swung clear of the pier legs and placed on a deck scow (fig. 132).

Three steel service girders and two sets of high-grade plywood shutters were used for the construction of the twenty-eight pier caps. It took three weeks to complete each pier cap.

Fig. 133 Pier work is finished and the "Ajax" floating crane moves the tower crane to the next pier site

Fig. 134 In the case of the high trestle piers, the 190-ton suspended spans were positioned by joint use of the "Ajax" and "Giraffe" floating cranes

Fig. 135   The 85m spans on the western side

235m Spans

Since the bridge had to provide ample shipway for ocean-going tankers to and from the important Venezuelan oilfields located at the head of the lake, five 235m centre spans were built. Horizontal clearance is 200m and the headroom is 45m. To exclude any possible damage resulting from differential settlement of the bridge piers and towers, or from light earthquake shocks, these central spans, like all the others, had to be statically determinate systems. For purposes of constructional economy, one main span was divided into a cantilever section, while a suspended span, constructed of the same prefabricated members as used for the 85m and 46.60m spans, bridges the gap.

The trestle pier foundation width was governed by the need for transferring the longitudinal bending moments, resulting from placing the suspended spans and from unsymmetrical traffic loads, to the ground in such a way that total costs for

Fig. 136   Main spans under construction

foundations and superstructure would be a minimum. The most economical width thus found was 34.60m in the centre line of the bridge. Since the horizontal clearance was specified as 200m, the cantilever arm length beyond the pile cap is (200 − 46) : 2 = 77m. To avoid an otherwise necessary but uneconomical depth of the cantilevers, in spite of this high amount of cantilevering, the tied cantilever construction method was resorted to. The cantilever span is therefore supported by inclined ropes suspended from the top of a 92.50m high tower. Any other system of support would have infringed upon the specified clearance.

Principles of Structural Analysis

Assumed hinges reduced the highly statically indeterminate system of the piers to a three times indeterminate principal system, namely, two-hinged frame with latticed legs and additional support of the cantilever arms (fig. 137). In this simplified hinged system, the intersecting forces were firstly computed by the method of elimination of geometrical elements. Torsions of the junctions in the hinged system were the basis for computing in a second operation the moments of constraint in the pier legs and in the tower by the deformation method. In this way, the actually flexurally-rigid junctions were taken into account as such. Because of the great rigidity differences, however, these secondary forces were small compared with the main forces computed for the simplified hinged system. Therefore, the influence ordinates computed for the hinged system accorded with the measurements taken on the two-dimensional reduced model (1:100) and the three-dimensional reduced model (1:50). These model tests

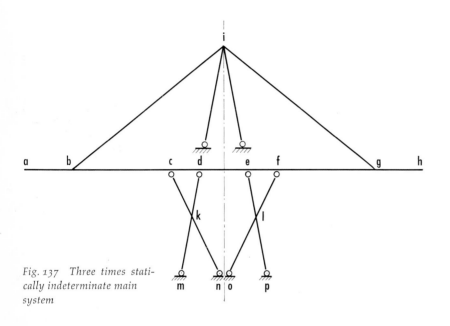

Fig. 137 Three times statically indeterminate main system

Fig. 138 Three-dimensional model. Scale 1/50th size

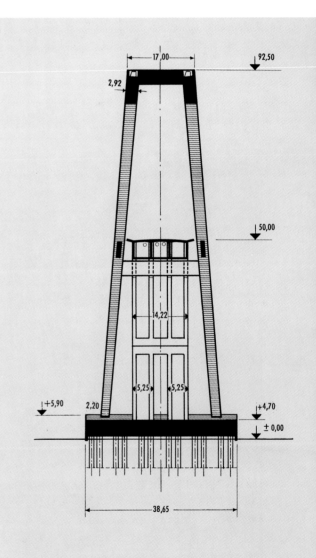

Fig. 139 Main span tower and "X"-frames

86

were carried out by the "Laboratorio Nacional del Engenha-ría Civil", Lisbon (fig. 138).

The cantilever span rests on "X"-frames (fig. 139). The relatively short distance between the legs of such a frame compared with the cantilever length results in almost rigid restraint. The cantilever span is supported by inclined ropes suspended from the top of a 92.50m high four-legged structure of two inclined "A"-frames linked at the top by a transverse girder. The four legs of this tower are nowhere connected with either the cantilever span or with the "X"-frames. The continuous cantilever girder is a closed box section, 5m deep. Its high torsional stiffness effectively distributes unsymmetrical traffic loads. In addition, the high natural torsional frequency of the box section avoids resonance with the natural frequency of the ropes.

Since strains of the ropes were equalized during construction, the intersecting forces of the system resulting from deadweight were calculated on the assumption of infinitely rigid inclined ropes. For traffic loads, however, elasticity of the ropes had to be taken into account. Due to the relatively flat slope of the ropes, an axial force was induced into the cantilever girder allowing mild steel reinforcement in nearly all parts of it. Additional tendons were only required in the girder above the "X"-frames and the prestressed transverse girders for anchoring the suspension ropes in order to account for moment raisers.

The structural analysis for the various stages of construction had to be done very carefully. This analysis involved five times more work than the structural analysis for the completed structure.

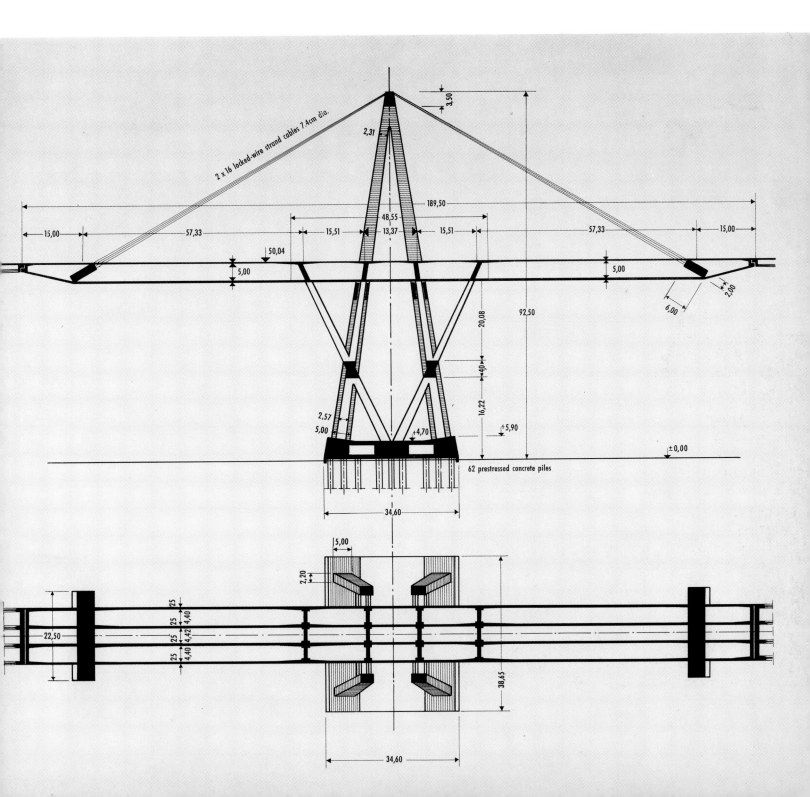

Fig. 140 *Part of the precast shuttering bottom for a pile cap of a main span is installed. Reinforcement is being placed in this part*

Pile Caps

In view of the weight of the structure, each main pier and tower of the long spans rests on sixty-two inserted piles flexurally-rigidly capped by a heavy concrete slab 34.60m wide in the centre line of the bridge, and 39m in the transverse direction, with a thickness of 4.7m over the central section sloping up to 5.90m at the fore and aft edges (figs. 140 and 141). One pile cap contains 5,100 m³ of 4,266-psi concrete (B 300) and 400 tons of reinforcing steel. Again, the reinforced concrete bottom shuttering was cast on shore. Each shuttering unit of a pile cap required twenty precast slabs of 50 to 60 tons each. The different lengths of the piles were equalized by varying the lengths of the suspensions for the precast slabs.

The pile cap had to be poured in five layers in order to avoid local overstressing. Two floating plants of 40 m³/h capacity each were used for concrete fabrication and pouring.

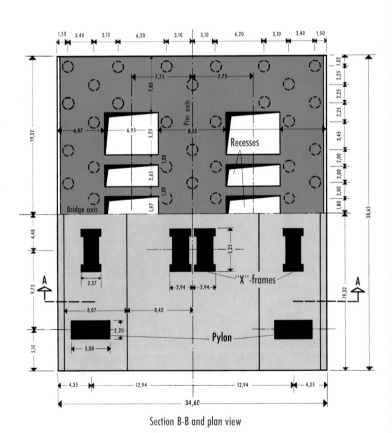

Section B-B and plan view

Fig. 141 *Pile cap for main span*

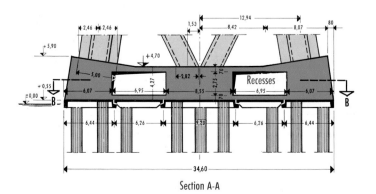

Section A-A

88

Equipment and Machinery for Construction of Main Spans

A bridge pier, a tower and a continuous cantilever girder required about 10,000 m³ of concrete and 800 tons of reinforcing steel. Materials for the tower had to be lifted up to 92.5m and materials for the cantilever girder conveyed up to 94m horizontal distance.

Two tower cranes were mounted on each pile cap. For the first stage of construction, the crab of the main crane lifted 4 tons at the end of the 40m jib at 69m hook height. This crane was later extended to 98m hook height for constructing the upper half of the tower. A second tower crane was installed on the other side for placing and removal of shuttering, placing reinforcement and concreting the "X"-frames and the lower half of the tower (fig. 142). Other tower cranes were mounted on the service girders of the cantilever arms. All these cranes were assembled on land and placed as one unit by floating cranes.

Concrete for the "X"-frames and the lower halves of the towers was poured by tower cranes using concrete skips. For construction of the continuous cantilever girders and the upper halves of the towers, a transfer hopper was installed at a height of 50m and fed by a concrete hoist. Power buggies took the concrete from this hopper to the forms, or the concrete for the upper part of a tower was lifted by the extended tower crane in skips.

A man-hoist was also installed.

Three generating sets, one compressor with a large air receiver, and a high-capacity water pump were installed on each pile cap. Power, compressed air, and water were distributed by cables and pipework.

Fig. 142   Structure 22, in the foreground, carries extended main tower crane (100m high), concrete hoist and man hoist. On the adjoining structure 23, the lifting operations for the rear service girder are proceeding. Front service girder already mounts a tower crane. The pier cap of structure 24 is poured and small tower crane is ready for dismantling. At structure 25 in background, concrete pouring for the "X"-frames and the lower half of the tower is carried out by two tower cranes

Fig. 143 *Pouring concrete for "X"-frames and tower. One of the two big floating concrete fabrication plants of 40 m³/h capacity each is seen on the left*

"X"-frames

The "X"-frames are of double T-girder section (fig. 143). While having an equal width of 5.25m from bottom to top transversely to the centre line of the bridge, the width in the direction of the bridge tapers from 2.57m at the bottom to 1.38m at the top. Two adjacent "X"-frames are tied at their junctions by a cross beam.

Climbing shutters of the Luchterhand type were used for the "X"-frames (figs. 143 and 144). The reinforcing cages were again fabricated on land in a length of 9.5m and placed into position by a tower crane. 6,399-psi concrete (B 450) was used for the "X"-frames and towers.

The structural analysis for the various conditions showed that during concreting the inclined legs had to be supported at

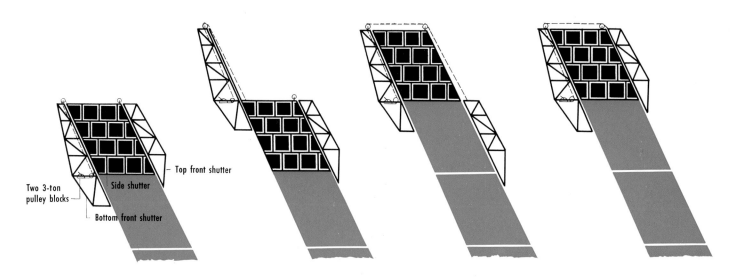

Fig. 144 Luchterhand type climbing shutters

Two 3-ton pulley blocks

Top front shutter

Side shutter

Bottom front shutter

1. *Concrete has hardened. Shutters are ready for raising.*
   1 Two 3-ton pulley blocks
   2 Bottom front shutter
   3 Top front shutter
   4 Side shutter

2. *Bottom front shutter is being detached from lost anchorage*

3. *Side shutters are then raised*

4. *Top front shutter completes the box shuttering*

a definite spacing so as to keep stresses and deformation within permissible limits (fig. 145). Before concreting the third section, inclined braces were installed and preloaded up to 20 tons by 100-ton hydraulic jacks. Higher up, the outer braces were tied by members each composed of six prestressing rods. Rod diameter is 26mm and ultimate strength of steel was from 80 to 105 kg/mm². Each rod was prestressed by a 35-ton jack to the statically required load. The rods rested on tubular centring to avoid vibration. The stresses in the rods were continuously checked and adjusted by the jacks.

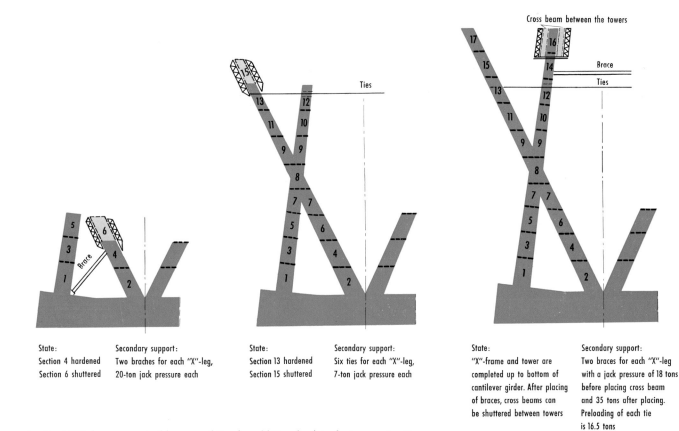

Cross beam between the towers

Ties

Brace

Ties

State:
Section 4 hardened
Section 6 shuttered

Secondary support:
Two braches for each "X"-leg,
20-ton jack pressure each

State:
Section 13 hardened
Section 15 shuttered

Secondary support:
Six ties for each "X"-leg,
7-ton jack pressure each

State:
"X"-frame and tower are
completed up to bottom of
cantilever girder. After placing
of braces, cross beams can
be shuttered between towers

Secondary support:
Two braces for each "X"-leg
with a jack pressure of 18 tons
before placing cross beam
and 35 tons after placing.
Preloading of each tie
is 16.5 tons

Fig. 145 Inclined "X"-frames required braces and ties for additional safety during construction

Fig. 146   Tower of a main span

Towers

Each tower is a four-legged structure of two inclined "A"-frames linked at the top by a transverse girder. Height is 92.5m (fig. 146).

The cross section changes with increasing height from 4.96m by 2.20m at the bottom to 2.31m by 2.92m at the top. This unusual shape complicated shuttering and reinforcement and called for close checking of the alignment.

Therefore, it was not possible to resort to the shuttering method used for the "X"-frames. For the towers, the shuttering had to be of box type with guide frames, so that its shape could continuously be adjusted by screw jacks to the variation of the tower cross-section (fig. 147).

Like the "X"-frames, the inclined tower legs also had to be braced during construction (fig. 148). To facilitate this bracing, the "X"-frames were erected sufficiently ahead of the towers, so that they could be used for bracing the towers.

Stage of construction:
Section 5 concrete hardened
Section 6 shuttered

Bracing:
Longitudinal brace preloaded 20 tons
Transverse braces between tower and
"X"-frame preloaded 35 tons each

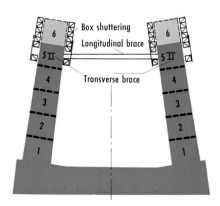

92

Fig. 147 *Climbing shuttering of a tower. The box shuttering is raised by toothed racks which bear against girders. These girders were fixed to lost anchorages*

Fig. 148 *Construction stages of a tower*

Stage of construction:
Section 10 and cross beam
between legs shuttered and concreted

Bracing:
Longitudinal brace preloaded 95 tons
Transverse braces preloaded 36 tons each

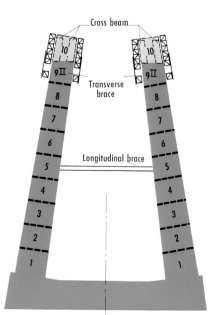

Cross beam

Transverse brace

Longitudinal brace

Stage of construction:
Section 15 concrete hardened
Section 16 shuttered

Bracing:
Transverses braces
preloaded 10 tons each

Transverse brace

Shore-fabricated longitudinal beam placed by floating crane

Stage of construction:
Section 18 concreted left side
Section 20 shuttered

Bracing:
Bottom transverse brace at right preloaded 20 tons
Bottom transverse brace at left preloaded 50 tons
Longitudinal brace preloaded 75 tons
Top transverse brace at right preloaded 30 tons

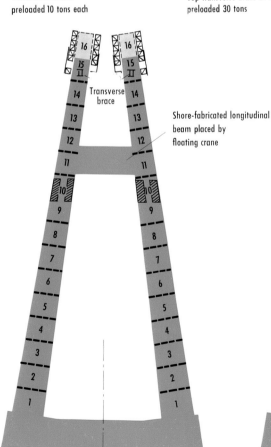

Top transverse brace

Longitudinal brace

Bottom transverse brace

93

Fig. 149   Cap of pier 20 is concreted. Service girder for cantilever arm is being raised

Pier Caps

The pier cap is a triple box section, 5m deep, 14.22m wide and 48.55m long (figs. 149 and 150). The "X"-frames are continued in the centre part of the cap as cross girders. The centre part of the cap is prestressed in the longitudinal and transverse directions. After having completed the centre part, the service girders for the cantilever arms were raised into position. At one end, they were lifted by the "Ajax" floating crane and at the other end by winches installed at the ends of the centre part of the cap. During this stage of construction, additional moments originated in the cap which required concentric prestressing.

Shuttering for the pier caps was the same as for the caps of the 85m spans (see page 78). By using service girders, ver-

tical centring of 40m height could be avoided (fig. 150). Horizontal ties prevented overstressing of the inclined legs (figs. 151 and 152).

Contrary to the 85 m spans, the different spacing of the legs required a service girder to be divided into three sections, each of which had to be placed separately (figs. 153 and 154). Placing the middle portion proved especially difficult, since the tower crane, concrete hoist and man-hoist infringed upon the available space. After concreting, the service girders were pulled out in sections sideways from underneath the cap, loaded on scows by a floating crane and brought to the shore for preparation for re-use.

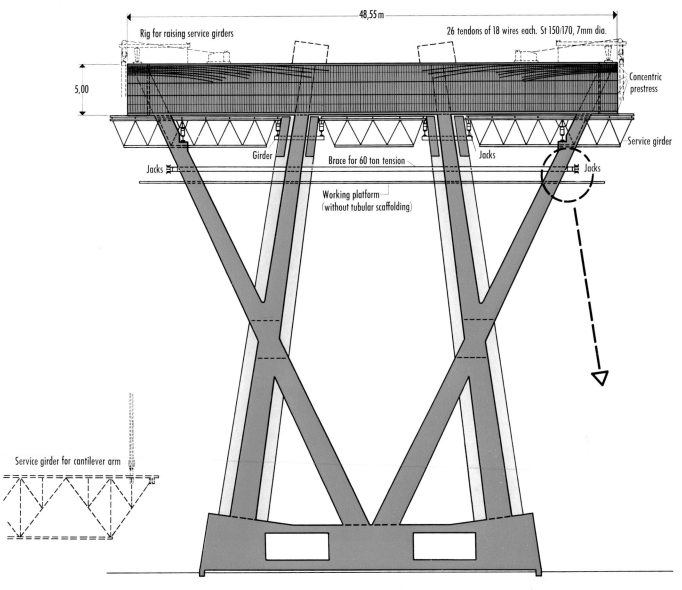

Fig. 150   Pier cap of a main span and service girder

Fig. 151   Two men check the jacks supporting the service girder (top). Rolled steel sections IP 30 serve as ties between "X"-frames. In the foreground, hydraulic control equipment for the jacks below service girder and for the ties

Fig. 152   Tension members bear against "X"-frames by being preloaded by hydraulic jacks

Fig. 153 The "Giraffe" floating crane lifts middle portion of a service girder from scow to pier. Shuttering and reinforcement were assembled on the service girder on land. This girder also houses the site office for the pier cap site

Fig. 154 Service girder is being placed in position. One of the four jacks for aligning the girder is seen in the foreground. In the background, there can be seen the girder on which the service girder will be placed (see fig. 151 top). This girder protrudes from the pier side. It is on this girder that after concreting and lowering the jacks the service girder will be withdrawn laterally underneath the cap

Fig. 155   *Placing trussed steel centering for the cantilever girders. On the left, the two service girders are positioned and carry shore-fabricated shuttering and reinforcement and a tower crane. The first service girder for the right-hand cantilever girder is in place, while the second one is being raised by the "Ajax" floating crane on one side and winches on the other side. Its rocker piers are still attached to its bottom*

Cantilever Arms   With their 72m length, thes are the longest rope-supported cantilever girders in prestressed concrete ever made. Detailed investigations were carried out to achieve an economical design. The structural analysis for the various stages of the work proved especially difficult. To save time, centring, shuttering and reinforcement were again prepared on land to the utmost extent.

Special trussed steel centrings (service girders) were used, as was the case for the pier caps of the major spans. These centrings were suspended at one end from the completed pier cap and bear at the other end against auxiliary foundations by means of rocking piers.

97

Fig. 156 *The cantilever girders of structure 21 are being concreted (right). In structure 20, the inclined ropes are already and the rocking piers of the service girders raised into the horizontal and attached*

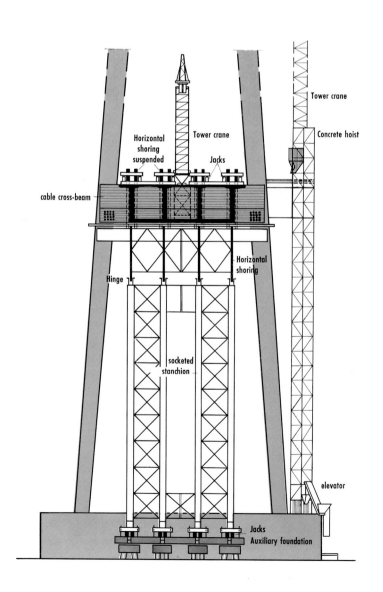

The cantilever arms were concreted in six sections to permit the equalization of deformation during concreting. Graphite lubricants between shuttering and service girders provided ready compensatory movement, so that no jerks occurred when lowering the service girders. After having concreted the last section of a cantilever arm, the hydraulic jacks mounted under the rocking piers raised or lowered the service girder to the theoretical elevation. The joints were then filled with concrete (figs. 156 and 157).

Prior to tensioning the inclined ropes, the jacking forces under the rocking piers were measured and the tensioning forces in the ropes were determined on that basis. Unintentional differences in deadweights of the cantilever arms could thus be equalized.

By tensioning the ropes, the load was gradually removed from the rocking piers. This procedure eliminated vertical displacement of the prestressed transverse girders for anchoring the suspension ropes. This requirement was fulfilled by lowering the jacks under the rocking piers in stages, so that elastic rebounds of the rocking piers and the rocking pier foundations were simultaneously equalized.

When the final rope was tensioned, the rocking piers were relieved of load. The horizontal component of the rope force then acted in the concrete of the cantilever arm as axial thrust.

The evaluation of the elasticity conditions in the cantilever girders on the one hand, and in the ropes on the other hand, was the crucial problem of cantilever arm design. Until the loads on the rocking piers were completely removed, conditions could be influenced by jacking under the rocking piers regardless of elasticity conditions. However, after the service girders had been lowered, this was no longer possible and thus any differences between actual and assumed moduli of elasticity caused additional deformation and stresses. To take care of this, the percentage of the mild steel reinforcement

of the cantilever arms was on the conservative side. This interim stage came to an end as soon as the gap between two cantilever arms was closed by the suspended span whose weight replaced the weight of the service girders.

During the various stages of construction, the calculated stresses and deformation were continuously checked. Permanent deformation of concrete and ropes had to be checked very carefully. The measured deformation differed but slightly from the design values.

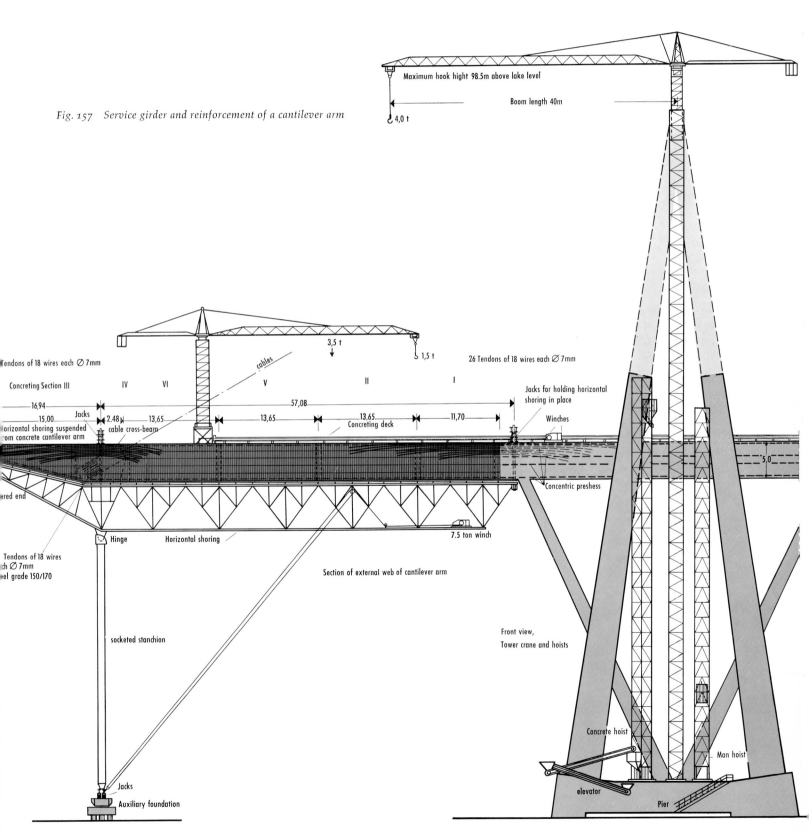

Fig. 157   Service girder and reinforcement of a cantilever arm

Fig. 158 Service girders are assembled in background. In the centre of the picture, shuttering and reinforcement is being installed on the two service girders. Service girder in foreground is ready for transport

Service Girders (Special Trussed Steel Centrings)

The service girders were made in Germany by the Joint Venture Demag-Gollnow, knocked down for transport, and reassembled on site (fig. 158). The steel used had 52 kg/mm² ultimate strength.

These girders were 6m deep and their length from the suspension at the cap to the rocking pier measured 57.08m. The cantilevered triangular-shaped end was 16.94m long. Each unit consisted of two trussed steel girders (fig. 159). Two units placed side by side were necessitated by the width of the bridge. On account of the short construction time, complete sets of service girders and shuttering for working simultaneously at two piers were required, that is, eight units totalling 2,200 tons. To compensate for deflection during concreting, the units were cambered 14m between their points of suspension at the caps and the hinges of the rocking piers.

Shuttering and reinforcement were placed on the service girder on shore (fig. 160). But owing to their weight, the girders

Fig. 159 The service girders were strengthened by box sections above the hinges of the rocker piers, so as to be able to support the heavy loads of the cable cross girders

Fig. 160 On the service girders, shuttering and reinforcement were installed on shore in about 13m long cages

could not be raised with all their shuttering and reinforcement. Therefore, only the reinforcement on the triangular-shaped cantilever was left in place, while the other four box shutterings were loaded on scows. A girder was moved on a track for sufficient distance into the harbour basin, so that a flooded twin scow could be positioned underneath. When the twin scow was pumped out, the girder was lifted from its dollies and was then tugged to the pier site.

Rocking Pier Foundations

Twenty spiral-welded steel pipes of 76cm dia. and ¹/₄in. wall thickness were driven for each rocking pier foundation. The 3m long pile points were filled with concrete to allow driving through sandstone. Pile lengths were determined by standard penetration tests and cone penetrometers. The piles, which were up to 41m long, were driven by a 15-ton hammer at a drop of 0.5m until at least 35 blows were necessary for 10cm of penetration.

The twenty piles were grouped in four bents and a prestressed pile-capping beam was placed on top (fig. 161). The two outer bents carried 806 tons each or 134 tons per pile, whereas the inside ones carried 658 tons each or 164 tons per pile. Settlement of the bents was continuously checked and compensated by jacking; it did not exceed 24mm.

Fig. 161 The rocking pier transfers its load by means of 16 jacks to its foundation

Fig. 162   *Transmitting the large forces from the inclined ropes into the prestressed transverse anchoring girders required heavy reinforcement. This cage-like reinforcement was made on shore*

Prestressed Transverse Girders for Anchoring the Inclined Bridge Ropes

The inclined bridge ropes are anchored in 22.5m long prestressed transverse girders whose section lies with its longitudinal axis in the direction of the suspension. The 60-ton reinforcing cages for these girders pere prepared on shore in the direction of suspension (figs. 162 and 164).

Ten steel frames were set on wooden templets. They served for placing the seventy prestressing cables, bracing the reinforcement and fastening the steel spreader bar. The thick-walled steel pipes for housing the suspension ropes were welded to steel plates at the top and bottom. Then, mild steel reinforcement and the prestressing cables were placed. The stressing heads were bolted to the steel front shuttering. A steel spreader bar made it possible to place reinforcing cages in the direction of the suspension (fig. 163).

All reinforcing cages were placed to such accuracy that deviations of the steel pipes for housing the suspension ropes were kept within 2cm of alignment.

Fig. 163   *The "Ajax" floating crane places a 60-ton reinforcing cage for a prestressed transverse anchoring girder*

Fig. 164 Preliminary work for the cantilever arms on shore. A reinforcing cage for a rope anchoring girder is being made in the foreground. A special trussed steel centring with shuttering and reinforcement for a cantilever arm can be seen in the background

Fig. 165 A cantilever arm during construction as seen from a tower. The section at the bottom of the picture is already concreted. Shuttering and reinforcement are being placed for the next sections

Fig. 166   A service girder is being raised into position at one end by four electric winches placed on the pier cap and at the other end by the "Ajax" floating crane (not seen in the picture). Winches lifted 120 tons, 180 tons being handled by the crane

Fig. 167   The second service girder is being lifted to its final height. The ropes will then be replaced by temporary tie rods. The height of these tie rods is adjusted by jacks placed on the deck (see fig. 157)

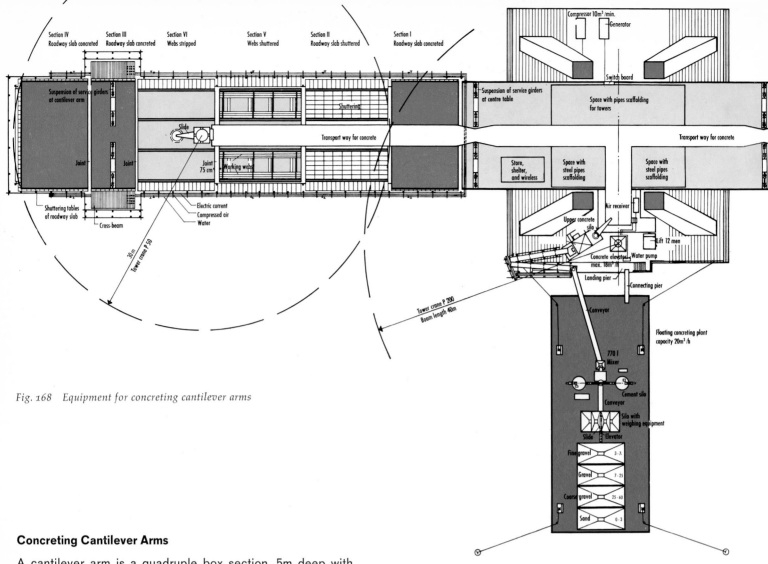

Fig. 168   Equipment for concreting cantilever arms

Concreting Cantilever Arms

A cantilever arm is a quadruple box section, 5m deep with 25cm thick walls. Its six sections were concreted in numerical sequence with a view to equalizing deformation (fig. 168). Furthermore, pouring concrete by sections had to proceed so that pier and cap would not be overstressed. 75cm wide joints were left open between the sections. They were filled after the trussed steel centering had been positioned by jacks under the rocking piers.

Concrete was fabricated by a floating mixing plant anchored alongside the pier, lifted by concrete hoist, conveyed power buggies to the tower crane for pouring by buckets (fig. 168).

The compression slab, the webs and the roadway slabs of the bgx section were concreted in sections so as to allow continuous placing of shuttering, reinforcement and concrete (figs. 165 and 169).

Fig. 169   Cantilever arm construction. Suspension of the service girder at the pier cap in foreground. Runway to tower crane for power buggies can be seen in middle of the cantilever arm

Fig. 170 Bridge ropes. Catwalks for mounting the ropes can be seen below them

Bridge Ropes

The bridge ropes were made by Messrs. Felten & Guilleaume with cold-drawn patented Siemens-Martin cast steel wires (figs. 170 and 171). The modulus of elasticity was determined by tests:

Force in rope	Modulus of elasticity ton/m²
0 to 32	1.0×10^7
31 to 118	1.3×10^7
118 to 120	1.7×10^7

The thirty-two ropes of a system have to carry a permanent load of 5,425 tons or 170 tons per rope plus fourteen tons traffic load. The breaking strength of a rope was determined as a result of four tests of 601 tons.

The ropes were cut to proper length and their conical ends poured in Germany. The conical ends had internal threads to accept the stretching screws. These ends were tested for tight fit by elongation and long-time tests.

Diameter of locked coil rope:	74mm
Load-carrying cross-section:	3,800mm²
Weight:	31.7 kg/m
Length — bottom layer:	188.85m
top layer:	188.85m

Fig. 171 Composition of a bridge rope

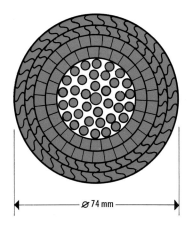

⌀74 mm

From inner layer to outer layer	Type and number of wires			Nominal tensile strength
	King wire	1	4.65 mm dia.	Blind wire
1	Round wires	6	4.28 mm dia.	160 kg/mm²
2	Round wires	12	4.28 mm dia.	160 kg/mm²
3	Round wires	18	4.28 mm dia.	160 kg/mm²
4	Wedge shaped wires	26 ▽	5.00 mm high	150 kg/mm²
5	Wedge shaped wires	32 ▽	5.00 mm high	150 kg/mm²
6	Full-lock wires	34 ∫	6.00 mm high	150 kg/mm²
7	Full-lock wires	38 ∫	6.00 mm high	150 kg/mm²

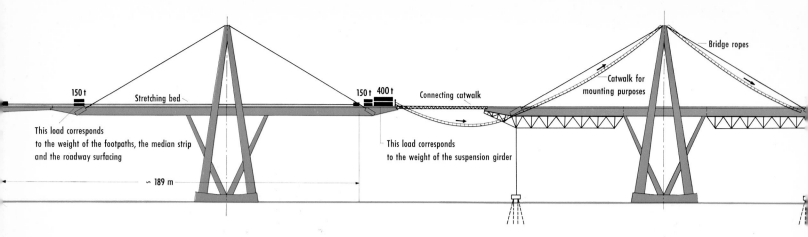

Fig. 172   Placing bridge ropes

150 t
Stretching bed
This load corresponds
to the weight of the footpaths, the median strip
and the roadway surfacing
~ 189 m
150 t   400 t   Connecting catwalk
This load corresponds
to the weight of the suspension girder
Bridge ropes
Catwalk for
mounting purposes

Catwalks for mounting the ropes were made on the shore, barged to the piers, and placed there on the caps by floating crane. One end of each catwalk was then raised by winches to the rope seat on the tower and anchored there (fig. 172). The other end was pulled to the prestressed transverse anchoring girder and fixed there.

The ropes, which were delivered in coils of 4m to 5m dia., were laid out on the roadway of the bridge, stretched, their length checked, cleaned, and given a prime coat. Subsequently, the ropes were threaded into the pipes of an anchoring girder, then pulled up the catwalk to a roller saddle support provided for mounting purposes on top of the tower, pulled down the catwalk on the other side, and threaded into the pipes of the opposite anchoring girder (figs. 172 to 174).

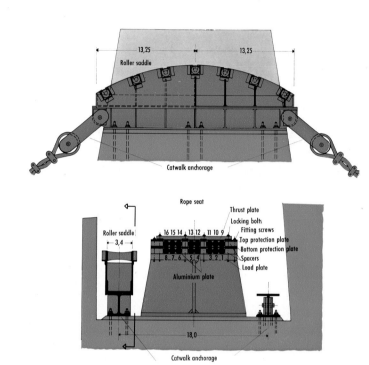

Fig. 173   Rope seat with roller saddle

Fig. 174   Threading a bridge rope into a pipe of the anchoring girder and rope stretching system

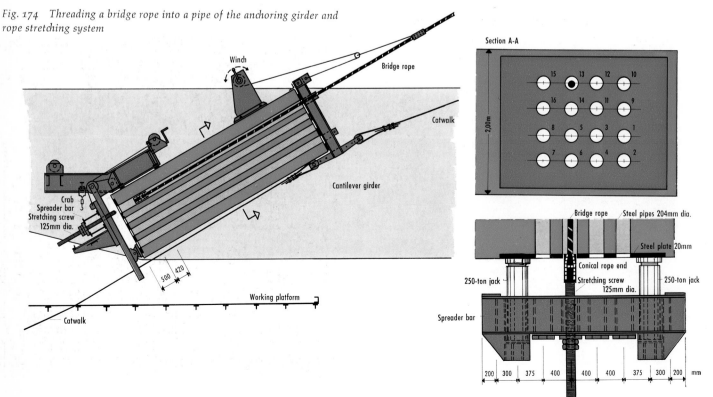

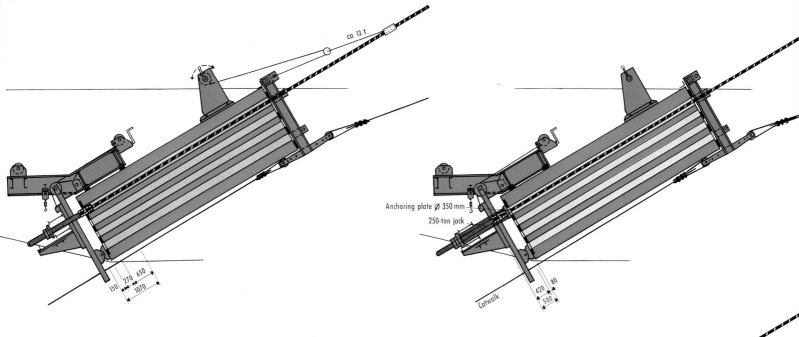

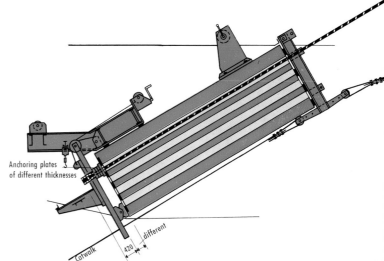

Anchoring plate Ø 350 mm
250-ton jack
Catwalk

Anchoring plates
of different thicknesses

Catwalk different

Fig. 175 a, b, c   Stretching bridge ropes

The ropes are arranged in the anchoring girders in four layers above each other, but in the rope seats in two layers above each other only. Two to three ropes were placed during daytime and stretched symmetrically during the following night. Stretching could only be done during the night in order to eliminate, so far as possible, the influence of temperature variations.

At first, each rope was stretched sufficiently by a hand winch and clamp, so that the rope end with the internal thread projected out of the anchoring girder by about 150mm (fig. 175a). This required a stretching force of about thirteen tons and left the rope sagging about 3.25m. The stretching screws of 125mm dia. could then be screwed into the internal thread of the conical rope ends.

Two 250-ton jacks pulled the rope out sufficiently to allow an 80mm thick washer to be inserted between conical rope end and anchoring girder (figs. 175b and 176). The washer was then welded to the anchor plate of the anchoring girder. The rope was now stretched to 106 tons; the sag was 31cm.

According to the theoretical force between 161 to 172 tons, the second jack operation was 10 to 12cm, after which the end was held in its final position by inserting additional washers. The sag was only about 20cm at a rope force of 170 tons (fig. 177).

As soon as the rope end was definitely in place, the force in the rope was checked by measuring the oscillations of the rope and corrected, if necessary. The stretching screw was then removed (fig. 175c).

Fig. 176   Stretching a bridge rope with two 250-ton jacks

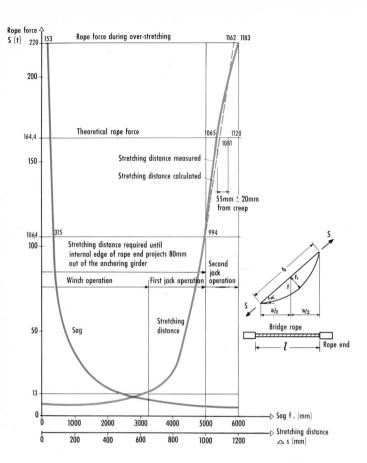

Fig. 177   Stretching distance, sag and force of a bridge rope

of the rope — solely on the dead weights of the ropes, the spans and the forces of the ropes. The accuracy of this measurement amounted to 2 to 3 per cent or 3 to 5 tons, which was entirely satisfactory.

Each rope, before finally fixing it in the anchoring girder, was over-stretched three times to 220 tons in order to eliminate the greater part of the so-called rope stretch. During this stretching, 35mm to 60mm permanent elongation was measured. It was found later, however, that this procedure alone was not sufficient to eliminate the permanent elongation.

As soon as the last pair of ropes of a pier was stretched, all rope forces were again checked by oscillation measurements. An average relaxation of the rope forces from 8 to 10 tons or 4.7 to 5.8 per cent was determined. These checks were carried out at night at a uniform temperature of the structure of 24° to 25° C. During the same night, before sunrise, the residual forces in the rocking piers were also measured, using precision gauges attached to the jacks under the rocking piers.

These measurements proved the relaxation of the forces in the ropes due to rope stretch. The ropes were re-stretched accordingly. Finally, the thrust plates of the rope saddles were placed and fixed by high-strength bolts (figs. 173 and 179).

As a first approximation, the forces in the ropes were determined on the basis of the forces exerted by the stretching jacks. The accuracy of measurement was 3 to 7 per cent or 5 to 12 tons. Jacks and gauges were calibrated before each use.

The forces in the ropes were checked by oscillations. A hemp rope was fixed at the lower third point of the steel wire rope, into which oscillations were induced by a man pulling the hemp rope. The time was taken for 100 oscillations (fig. 178). The number of oscillations depends — neglecting the stiffness

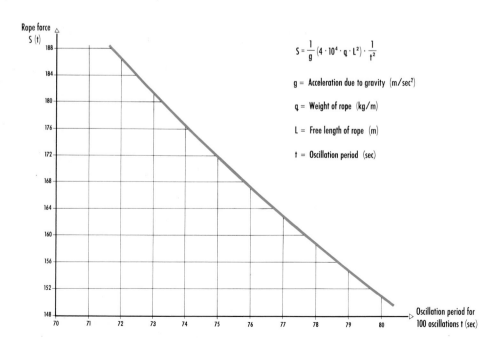

Fig. 178   Relationship between period of oscillation and rope force

$$S = \frac{1}{g} \left(4 \cdot 10^4 \cdot q \cdot L^2 \right) \cdot \frac{1}{t^2}$$

g = Acceleration due to gravity (m/sec²)

q = Weight of rope (kg/m)

L = Free length of rope (m)

t = Oscillation period (sec)

Fig. 179 The ropes are fixed in the rope saddle by high-strength bolts and thrust plate. Roller saddle used for placing ropes can be seen at left

Fig. 180 Bridge ropes were pulled on the catwalks up to the roller saddle and down the other side. Jacks forcing the service girder to the rope anchoring girder can be seen in foreground

Fig. 181 *The rocking pier of a service girder is attached to the latter. Service girder is ready for lowering on to twin barge*

Simultaneously with the stretching of the ropes, the anchoring girders were stretched in stages. It was only by observing a strict sequence of stretch between ropes and anchoring girders that tensile stresses in the concrete could be avoided. As soon as the rocking piers were completely relieved of load by stretching the ropes, the jacks under the rocking piers were removed to prevent the rocking piers from carrying any load again owing to elongations due to the temperature. A few hours later, the service girder was lowered about 20cm, thus breaking the bond between concrete and girder. The rocking piers were then lifted and secured (fig. 181).

The service girder was placed on the twin barge by the "Ajax" floating crane on the one end and the winches installed on the pier cap on the other (fig. 182).

Fig. 182 *A service girder is placed on the twin barge by the "Ajax" floating crane on the one end and the winches installed on the pier cap on the other*

Fig. 183   The "Ajax" and "Giraffe" floating cranes place a suspension girder

By removing the service girders, the rope forces were reduced by a total of 1,000 tons or 30 tons in each rope. To avoid redistributing the forces in the now partially unloaded system, concrete blocks of 550 tons total weight were stacked on each end of the cantilever arms (fig. 172). These blocks had to be arranged symmetrically with a view to avoiding the cantilever arms warping due to creep.

Before placing the suspension girders, an appropriate number of blocks was removed. On each end, however, 150 tons was left in place corresponding to the weight of the roadway surfacing and the side-walks. These blocks were removed according to the rate of progress of the surfacing work.

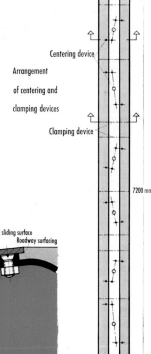

Fig. 184   Expansion joint between suspension girder and centre pier. The centrally placed bridging plate is held by centring devices and forced against the inclined sliding surfaces by clamping devices. All wearing parts can be replaced from above by using simple tools

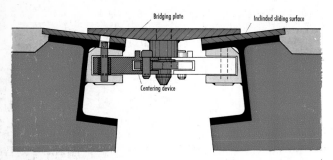

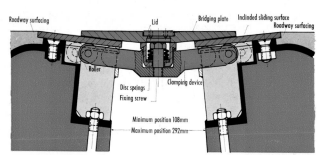

Fig. 185   Completed centre spans

Fig. 186   View of centre spans

Fig. 187   The "Ajax" and „Giraffe" floating cranes place the last of the suspension girders

General

Surveying

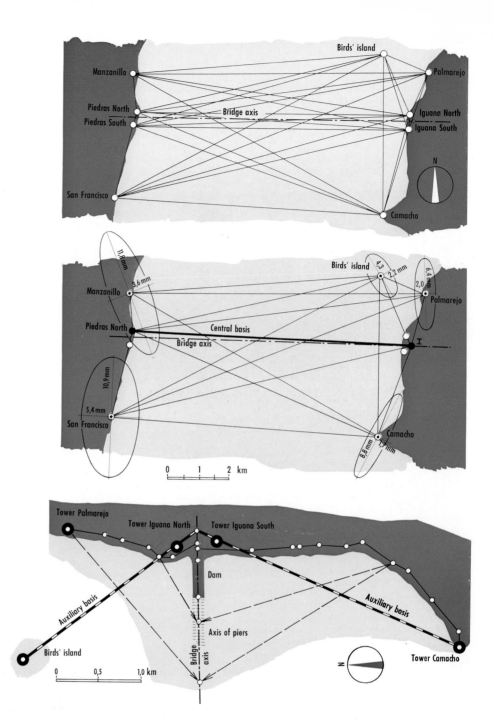

Fig. 188   Geodetic surveying

a) The triangles and all observed directions

b) The number of stations was reduced from nine to seven by centring calculations with a view to facilitating the conditioning. The ellipses of error show the mean error of the framework points

c) Secondary base lines were measured at the eastern shore of the Lake by precision traverses. After conditioning the angle, they were transferred to the base line. Before this, pegging was carried out from these traverses for fills, trial driving, and soundings

The bridge site extended over a length of about 8km. Construction operations were started and went on simultaneously at several widely separated points along the centre line of the bridge. Surveying therefore offered considerably greater difficulties than in the case of an ordinary bridge. The precast suspension girders called for an unusually high degree of accuracy.

Basic Survey

For the extensive and very exact survey, a skeleton framework of well-conditioned triangles was indispensable (fig. 188). Such a framework with nine trig. stations and a carefully measured base line from shore to shore was therefore considered to be the most suitable solution in view of the topo-

graphy. Each trig. station consisted of a tower of adequate height, so as to take into account the curvature of the earth and to prevent the 5m atmospheric disturbance layer from influencing the observations (fig. 189). Even over a distance of ten kilometres, the tangential curvature amounts to 7.84m. Tropical temperatures and high ambient humidity caused considerably refraction errors in the measurement of the angles. The most suitable hours for precision surveying during daytime and nighttime were found by extensive and continuous observations.

The base line of the main framework of large triangles differed only slightly from the centre line of the bridge (fig. 188b). Two procedures independend of each other were employed with a view to measuring the length of the base line as carefully as possible and eliminating error.

levels on both sides were observed by means of precision gauges for an extended period of time which allowed comparable gauge data to be fixed. The levels were then transferred trigonometrically. With a view to eliminating refraction influences, two-way observations were made from two towers simultaneously for a period of twenty-four hours. The measurement showed a difference in elevation for the two gauge data of 3.4cm. The mean error of level over the length of 9km was reduced to ± 4.7mm. During the construction of the piers, precision levellings were made from both shores, which showed a difference in level of 3.35cm at a mean error of ± 1.1mm. This difference was distributed over 19 piers over a length of 2,000m.

Detail Surveying

The centre line of the bridge could not be used for the surveying of the individual structures, since vision was obstructed by piers and large floating equipment units. Therefore, parallel centre lines were established on both sides which were marked on land by large triangles having a coat of contrasting paint. At nighttime, these triangles were illuminated. For detailed pegging out in the lake, the triangular steel towers used for the soil tests were used (fig. 32). The towers were placed by floating cranes and their locations determined from the trig. stations by using theodolites and the radio telephone.

Fig. 189 A trig. station. This is a cross-shaped concrete pier with the instrument platform. The core is protected against sun radiation and deformation due to temperature

Fig. 190 The tellurometer is an electro-magnetic distance meter. A radio telephone was used between the main and secondary stations. Wave length is 10cm or 3,000 mc/s at a range of 0.15 to 50 km. Accuracy of measurement is about 1/300,000

First, the base line was measured electronically by means of a tellurometer (fig. 190). Measurements were made at several hours day and night under different weather conditions with a view to determining as closely as possible their influence. Two secondary base lines established on the eastern shore were used for the confirmation of the length of the base line by the application of trigonometry (fig. 188c). A comparison of the two measurements showed a mean error of ± 31mm for the 8,871.834m long base line. After determining the length of the base line and measuring the angles, the ends of the base line were given final co-ordinates and the secondary stations temporary co-ordinates, which were later conditioned arithmetically.

Transferring the levels accurately from one shore to the other proved especially difficult. As a first approximation, the lake

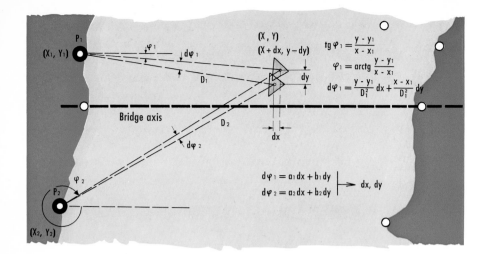

P_1
(X_1, Y_1)

φ_1
$d\varphi_1$

D_1

(X, Y)
$(X + dx, y - dy)$

dy

Bridge axis

D_2

$d\varphi_2$

dx

φ_2

P_2

(X_2, Y_2)

$\operatorname{tg} \varphi_1 = \dfrac{y - y_1}{x - x_1}$

$\varphi_1 = \operatorname{arctg} \dfrac{y - y_1}{x - x_1}$

$d\varphi_1 = \dfrac{y - y_1}{D_1^2} dx + \dfrac{x - x_1}{D_1^2} dy$

$d\varphi_1 = a_1 dx + b_1 dy$
$d\varphi_2 = a_2 dx + b_2 dy$ $\longrightarrow dx, dy$

Fig. 191 The angles with the towers erected in the lake were checked almost daily. The angle difference of two measurements and the distance enabled tables of the relevant corrections of the co-ordinates to be drawn up

Measurements of the Completed Structure

A test girder on land and the small piers, which were completed first, served to obtain the necessary data on the influence of temperature on forces and deformation within the structure, such data being required for the statical analysis of the 85m and 235m spans.

Settlements of the various bridge structures were checked by precision levellings and gauges. These checks are still carried on by Maracaibo Technical College.

Further investigations dealt with:

Variations in length of precast prestressed girders due to creep and shrinkage.

Distribution of temperature of the whole of a girder.

Movement of piers caused by placing the suspension girders. Dislocations and bending of "X"-frames and towers in the large spans.

Meteorological observations were necessary; e. g. to determine the index of refraction of the atmosphere. Planning and surveying the navigation channel, which frequently had to be relocated during the construction of the bridge, were also handled by the survey department.

Subsequently, the co-ordinates of a sight-mark on the tower weer determined by fore-sight from the same stations which had already been used for placing the tower (fig. 191). The X-co-ordinates were checked, if necessary, by direct distance measurement with the tellurometer. From the sight-mark on the tower, any point within 30m to 40m distance could be set out easily by the polar method.

The exact position of the piles had to be determined quickly, so that the bottom shuttering for the pile caps could be made without any loss of time. Terrestrial photogrammetry was used in the case of the large piers (fig. 192). Photographs of the piles were taken with a 36mm camera from a crane at a height of 30m to 50m. The negative was rectified by means of a projector on two tilting tables by the four-point method. In this way, thirty-two piles could be surveyed in one day at a mean error of 2.1cm.

Surveying the climbing shuttering for the piers and towers also proved difficult. For this purpose, panels with three-dimensional theoretical co-ordinates were used.

Fig. 192 The location of the piles for a big pier is determined by terrestrial photogrammetry

Testing Concrete and Construction Materials

Fig. 193   *Laboratory sieve sets and drying oven*

A field concrete laboratory started work one year before the actual construction began. Numerous preliminary tests were required for selecting the most suitable aggregates (fig. 193).

Standard Specifications
Cement, aggregates, and concrete were tested according to ASTM Standard Specifications. These are more exacting than DIN Standards. Only the DIN 1045 and 1047 grading curves were used, but the ASTM Sieve Numbers were retained. The German regulations and codes of practice for grout and additives were used.

Cement
Portland cement with a specification strength of 245 kg/cm^2 — ASTM type I — was used. The effective strength was between 350 to 420 kg/cm^2 with temporary decrease to 255 kg/cm^2. The percentage retained on the 0.074mm sieve (No 200) was 4.6.

Additives

When selecting additives, influence on the following properties had to be considered: workability, strength, initial set, setting time, hardening, and shrinkage. The following additives were used in respect of the above properties: —

Additive	Weight in per cent of cement	Use
Pozzolith 8	0.27	workability agent for precast concrete and grout
Tricosal VZ	0.18 to 0.35	retarder and workability agent for mass concrete and grout
Plastiment	0.10 to 0.20	retarder and workability agent

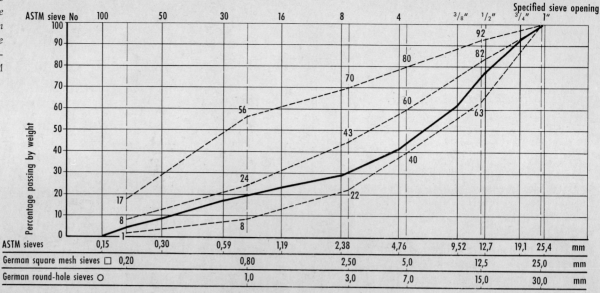

Fig. 194 Grading curve of the concrete for the big piers. The graduation limits of DIN 1045 are converted from round-hole sieves to the ASTM square mesh sieves

Aggregates

Sand:

The 0—3mm fraction was obtained from the lake. This material had to be washed. It contained:

grains smaller than 0.074mm (No 200 Sieve)   0.1 to 0.7 %

sulfate   0.005 to 0.03 %

chloride   0.005 to 0.01 %

Gravel:

Gravel was extracted in a deposit 62 km away from the site. It was delivered in the fractions 2 to 12mm, 12 to 25mm, and 25 to 60mm (fig. 31). Limestone chippings were brought to the site from the 45 km distant Isle of Toas in fractions of 4 to 10mm, 10 to 20mm, and 25 to 63mm.

Concrete

The specified minimum cement factor was 300 kg/m³ and the grading curve of the total aggregates was within the gradation limits D and E (fig. 194).

Compressive strength of concrete was determined in the beginning by using the best three of four cylinder test results whose average had to be higher than the specified strength. Later, the average of all four test results was determined (fig. 195).

The following tests were made: —

	no.
Concrete trial mixes	227
Mortar trial mixes	225
Cement tests	259
Lake sand tests	522
Limestone chipping tests	321
Gravel tests	338

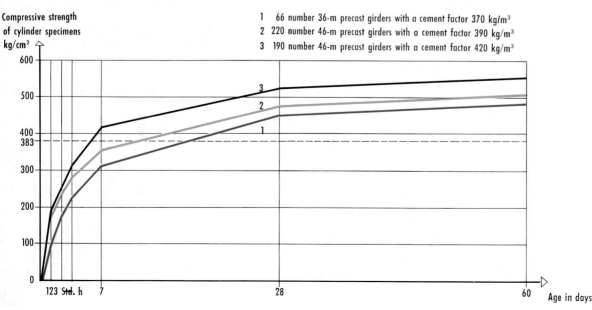

1 66 number 36-m precast girders with a cement factor 370 kg/m³
2 220 number 46-m precast girders with a cement factor 390 kg/m³
3 190 number 46-m precast girders with a cement factor 420 kg/m³

Fig. 195 Compressive strengths of concrete for the suspension girders

Fig. 196　A cylindrical specimen of 15.2cm dia. is placed in the testing machine

Fig. 197　Testing a beam specimen 15 x 15cm by two loads in the flexural strength testing machine

Test specimens comprised:　　　　　　　　　no.

Concrete cylinders 15.2cm dia. (fig. 196)	36,826
Mortar cylinders 10.5cm dia.	2,063
Cement cubes	1,737
Beam specimens (fig. 197)	253
Test cores	84

The concrete laboratory developed suitable mortar mixes for grouting the prestressing ducts and piles.

The grout for the prestressing ducts had to flow freely even at high temperatures. An average compressive strength of 585 kg/cm² was obtained after twenty-eight days with a water-cement ratio of 0.418 and Pozzolith 8 as an additive.

The initial set of the grout for skin grouting the piles had to be retarded by ten hours, so that any delay in withdrawing the casings due to a breakdown in machinery would not be harmful. Tricosal VZ was used as a retarder.

The grout for pile point grouting was subjected to pressures up to 40 kg/cm². In spite of the high temperatures, it was not allowed to clog the 1″ pipes which were about 50m long. This requirement was fulfilled only when Halliburton cement was used. At a water-cement ratio of 0.41, a compressive strength of 616 kg/cm² was obtained.

Statistical interpretation of the compressive strength results										
Item	Concrete		No of speci-mens	Specified Strength		Actual mean strength		①	②		Coeff. of variation
	m³	cby		kg/cm²	psi	kg/cm²	psi		kg/cm²	psi	%
Pile sections	2.132	2.789	1.067	468	6.656	542	7.709	1,16	32,6	463	6,02
46 m girders	2.130	2.786	69	383	5.447	431	6.130	1,13	29,9	425	6,9
46 m girders	6.760	8.842	215	383	5.447	540	7.680	1,41	34,0	484	6,29
Pile cap, pier 21	5.160	6.749	53	255	3.627	463	6.585	1,82	56,1	798	12,1
"X"-frames and tower, pier 21	6.364	8.324	158	383	5.447	475	6.756	1,24	38,5	548	8,1
"X"-frames and tower, pier 23	6.364	8.324	148	383	5.447	463	6.585	1,21	27,8	395	6,0
Pier cap and cantilever arms, pier 20	3.226	4.220	124	383	5.447	498	7.083	1,30	50,7	721	10,2
Pier cap and cantilever arms, pier 21	3.226	4.220	101	383	5.447	492	6.998	1,29	28,2	401	5,7
Pier cap and cantilever arms, pier 22	3.226	4.220	109	383	5.447	491	6.983	1,28	30,4	432	6,2

① = Ratio of actual to specified strength　　② = Mean variation

Fig. 198 Mixing plant of 20 m³/h capacity mounted on a 900-ton deck scow. Concrete is conveyed by swivelling elevating belt conveyor

Mixing Plant

Climatic conditions and high stresses called for high-quality concrete. The mixing plants were therefore periodically checked as to reliable scales, water measuring devices, uncontaminated stockpiles, and other fundamental facilities. The maximum temperatures allowed were 50° C for cement and 24° C for concrete.

One stationary and seven floating mixing plants produced about 270,000m³ of concrete (figs. 198 and 199).

Mixing plant no	Operation	Mixers no	type	Capacity m³	Output per hour m³
1	semi-automatic	2	tilting drum	1.5	80
2, 3	manual	1	free-fall	0.45	12
4 ,5, 6	manual	1	free-fall	0.77	20
7, 8	semi-automatic	1	pug mill	1.5	30 to 40

Fig. 199 Mixing plant of 30 m³/h to 40 m³/h capacity mounted on a 1,800-ton deck scow. Concrete is lifted by skip 7m high to the 18m long swivelling belt conveyor

Output and Equipment

This remarkable structure could not be accomplished by a handful of men. From planning to financing, from design to construction, a great number of Venezuelan and European engineers worked jointly in Wiesbaden, Caracas, Rome, Maracaibo, Zürich, Paris, and Lisbon. In this way, one of the most outstanding structures of our time was erected within the stipulated — and brief — construction time.

The quotation was 265,775,443 Bolivars down.

Additional work amounted to about 45,000,000 Bolivars.

This consisted in:

a) Excess pile lengths due to locally poor subsoil.

b) Ancillary work such as, for instance, lighting the navigation channel, etc., which had not been included in the contract.

c) Work which was included in the contract but whose scope could not be determined in advance, such as soil exploration and tests, load tests, ect.

d) Reimbursement of additional social security charges which arose after the contract had been signed.

Fig. 200   Preparatory works on shore

Pfähle Piles

Total amount of work done:

35,660 rm piles placed in pre-drilled holes 135 cm dia.
27,170 rm driven piles, 91.4 cm dia.
6,260 rm driven piles, 50 x 50 cm.

Beton Concrete

11,000 m³ concrete for driven piles
23,500 m³ concrete for piles placed in pre-drilled holes
32,000 m³ concrete for filling hollow piles
40,600 m³ concrete for precast elements
156,000 m³ in-situ concrete for superstructures
6,900 m³ concrete for auxiliary structures
270,000 m³ total amount of concrete

Stahl Steel

3,000 tons steel centring
800 tons tubular steel scaffolding
19,000 tons reinforcing steel, grade IIa
5,000 tons prestressing wire for Morandi and
Philipp Holzmann A.G. prestressing systems
1,400,000 rm of sheet-metal sheaths
36,680 rm bridge ropes 74 mm dia.

Fig. 201 Large equipment at work

Equipment worth 60 million Bolivars had to be employed in view of beating the short target date. The main equipment items were:

  3 working platforms, one with a crane of 250 tons capacity
  3 floating cranes of 60 to 250 tons capacity
13 cranes mounted on scows and piers
10 tower cranes with hook heights up to 98.5 m, length of boom up to 40 m and 1.5 to 15 ton capacity
  1 electric gantry of 52 m span, 14 m hoist height and two 100-ton crabs
  1 gravel and screening plant of 30 ton/h capacity
  8 reverse circulation drilling rigs with rotating tables
31 tugs and motor boats
48 deck scows
37 outboards
39 vehicles of various types
11 forklift trucks and bulldozers
53 generators
23 transformers
31 air compressors
329 concrete vibrators of various types
57 welding transformers and welding sets

Fig. 202   View of the site camp

Apart from this concentration of large and modern equipment, a large working force had to be employed because work was going on all the time at many places simultaneously. During the main construction period, 2,630 men were employed on the average, of whom 173 were foremen, 1,048 skilled, and 1,026 unskilled, workmen, and 225 white collar workers.

Table of Contents

Compilation: Dr.=Ing. Hanns Simons, Heinz Wind, W. Hans Moser

Artwork: Erika Peleska-Dietl, Hamburg-Blankenese

Photography: by the site photographers J. J. Castro 22, 23, 26, 27, 30, 31, 33, 38, 40, 43, 49, 52, 56, 59, 65, 66, 69, 72, 73, 77, 80, 86, 95, 96, 98, 100, 102, 103, 104, 107, 108, 110, 114, 115, 119, 122, 124, 126, 127, 128, 133, 134, 135, 136, 140, 142, 143, 146, 147, 149, 151, 152, 153, 154, 155, 156, 158, 159, 160, 161, 162, 163, 166, 167, 169, 170, 176, 181, 182, 183, 186, 187, 193, 199, 200, 202.

Messrs C. A. Constructora Heerema, P. Heerema, Maracaibo: 67, 71

H. G. Henneberg: 190, 192

R. Jetter: 165, 179, 180

Laboratório Nacional del Engenharia Civil, Lisbon: 138

W. Nordmann: 196, 197

H. Ramm: 185

Bild= und Filmstelle Salzgitter=Maschinenbau=AG., O. Richter: 97, 118, 129, 164, 189

H. Simons: 28, 60, 62, 64, 70, 90

W. Wachter: 1, 2, 3 aus „Venezuela — Land der Gegensätze", Büchergilde Gutenberg, Zürich

H. Wind: 79, 81, 83, 86, 87, 94, 105, 198

Printed by: Th. Dingwort & Sohn, Hamburg-Altona

Clichés: W. Uhrmacher, Hamburg
      Albert Bauer KG, abc-clichés, Hamburg —
      clichés of the coloured photographs

Bound by: Hilge Harten, Hamburg-Altona

English by: H. Bucksch, Köln, H. Brückner, Wächtersbach